Mark Waller's

Harmonics

A Field Handbook
for the Professional
and the Novice

The Waller Group, Inc.
2222 Foothill Blvd., Suite 288
La Canada, California 91011
Phone: (818) 957-2266
FAX: (818) 957-2293

PROMPT® Publications is an imprint of Howard W. Sams & Company, 2647 Waterfront Parkway, East Drive, Suite 300, Indianapolis, IN 46214-2041.

International Standard Book Number: 0-7906-1048-5

Acquisitions Editor: *Candace M. Drake*
Editor: *Natalie F. Houck*
Assistant Editor: *Rebecca A. Hartford*
Illustrators: *Doug Cobb, Sara Wright*
Typesetter: *Leah Marckel*
Cover Designer: *Sara Wright*

Printed in the United States of America

Contents

Acknowledgements

This book would not have been possible without the contributions of many people.

To all of the folks at Howard W. Sams a debt is owed. Thanks to Damon Davis for keeping the relationship alive through thick and thin. Thanks to Kevin Etter for his pursuit of the marketplace—without him there would have been no book. Natalie Houck has been a joy to work with and her voice over the phone helped in those long final days. Thanks, too, to Candy Drake for picking up the ball so many times and running with it. Finally, were it not for the amazing efforts of Doug Cobb, the final product would never have looked so good.

There are many in the power quality community who have given self-lessly to this project. Top of the list is Craig Waterman of BMI who first recognized the importance of my writing this book. Ken Price and especially BMI's Mark Anderson were always willing to share information and respond to my requests.

This book gave me the opportunity to meet the professionals at John Fluke. Thanks to Robert Hamilton for opening the door, and to Bill Rasnick and Dick Troberg for stepping through with generous offers of assistance. An extra special thanks to Chuck Newcombe for coming through in a big way.

Appreciation goes out to Michael Lowenstein of TCI, Doug Dorr of the National Power Lab, and Murray Leonard of Best Power Technology. I would also like to thank John Mungenast and Myron Miller of *Power Quality Magazine* for providing *The Official Proceedings of Power Quality*. This is an amazing body of work that proved to be an invaluable reference for this book.

I am very grateful to three of my colleagues for doing a technical review of this book: Warren Lewis, Peter Gross, and Fred Stich. Their input was extremely valuable.

Special personal thanks go to Kate Adams for editorial help, support, and friendship throughout. One final note of acknowledgment. A long time ago during a very dark hour, Bill Sgro helped me when no one else could or would—thanks.

Finally, thanks to the hundreds of you who have attended the classes and workshops where I have been privileged to be a guest speaker. Your feedback and support have been invaluable.

Introduction

A few years ago, I attended a conference in which the kickoff speaker salt-and-peppered his address with the term "harmonics." Whenever a dramatic point was made, a phrase like "... and even harmonics," or "... big problems like harmonics," or "... achieving world peace, curing cancer, and solving harmonics" was used. It soon became apparent that all it took to appear knowledgeable in the field of power quality was to use the term harmonics often enough. Back then there was growing awareness that harmonics was a problem. Today it has reached a fever pitch, yet I still have people coming up to me after seminars to ask if harmonics will make the lights go out or cause their 56 Chevy to shimmy when it goes over 55 MPH. Obviously, harmonics is a mystery to many and it may rank as second only to El Nino as the cause behind all unsolved mysteries. Everyone in the electrical, facilities, power quality, and computer community is becoming aware that there is something called harmonics.

Today, people are not willing to settle for jargon being tossed around. They really want to know what "this harmonics stuff" is, and what (if anything) can be done about it. Interestingly enough, for a long time I considered approaching my publishers about a book on harmonics. I didn't, simply because I thought the topic was too technical to pique their interest. Ironically, at the same time, one of their executives was making the rounds on a field trip and asking each representative or distributor what book topics were being requested. "Harmonics" was the universal answer. It seems that there was a need beyond adding another buzz word to the electrical vocabulary.

The news made me happy, but I was not surprised. For several years I had been doing workshops for electrical utilities, manufacturers, and universities. One surefire way to fill a room was to put "harmonics" in the workshop title. Why such a hot topic? The short answer is that product technology and building technology have been on a collision course for some time. It seems that every time we try to do something positive for the building environment, something bad happens. Harmonics is a prime example. We are now installing all kinds of demand-side management products: VFDs, electronic lighting ballasts—new technologies right and left. Meanwhile, buildings are being stuffed with a vast array of single and three phase microprocessor-based devices, from computers to building systems. The burden of making this work together has fallen to a few dedicated professionals.

As a result of my speaking career, I got to know the professionals who are most interested in the topic—facility managers, electrical contractors, and maintenance personnel. I like these people. They are very real. They truly appreciate the few opportunities they get to increase their knowledge, and they sincerely want to put that knowledge into practice on the job. Also, they take harmonics seriously. They are individuals who will go back and tell their managers, engineers, and MIS people that there is an issue to deal with—"You got a problem with that?" These are my kind of guys, and this book has been written for them.

For me, writing this book was a bit of a dilemma. The principles of electricity, as they relate to harmonics, are rooted in mathematics—higher mathematics. In fact, one of the early books I found on the subject was at least 40% equations with a lot of Greek letters. I knew that the audience I most wanted to reach would not respond to a lot of heavy math or detailed techno-jumble. On the other hand, the information had to be accurate enough to stand up to the scrutiny of my peers in the power quality/power conditioning community. It reminds me of the evaluations I get after a workshop. If I get just as many complaints that I was too technical as I do that I was not technical enough, I feel I've done a good job!

The bottom line is that this book is intended for anyone with an understanding of Ohm's law and other basics about electricity and building power. My goal is that the individual—you—can pick up this book, read it easily, and get a fundamental understanding of the theories, issues, and scope of the harmonic problem and be ready to interface with engineers, sales reps, and managers to implement studies and solutions. For those who want more detail, let me refer you to the bibliography. Many of the books, and certainly the IEEE standards, are essential reading. Check out harmonic analyzer manufacturers for courses. BMI, Dranetz, and Fluke (to name a few) have schools, and excellent materials and videos.

A Special Note To Readers:

I have been doing harmonic studies and analysis for years, and many of the examples shown in this book are from those studies. I wanted to use as many "real world" examples as possible to give the book more authenticity and greater variety. Unfortunately, this necessitated the use of photocopies of printouts that were never intended to be photo-ready for a book. The fine people at Howard W. Sams took my field readings and duplicated, digitized, and hand reproduced them. They turned out great! Please don't be deceived by the quality of these graphics, and don't be put off that they don't look precisely like the original tapes from an analyzer. All were adapted from field readings I took unless otherwise noted in the caption, and every effort was made to preserve the exact waveforms that were on the original printout. Logos from manufacturers were retained to insure proper credit for the original output instrument source.

How To Use This Book

The world is changing—the electrical world, that is. Harmonics has become an everyday part of everyone's vocabulary in the electrical world. Much has been written about the subject, but not much of that information has started at square one. That's where this book starts.

Chapter 1 begins with the assumption that the reader has no concrete idea what harmonics is. From that point, every effort was made to develop the information logically. We start with single phase harmonics and move toward three phase harmonics. There are two reasons for this. First, single phase harmonics is a life/safety issue. A safe workplace is critical and cannot be sacrificed. Single phase harmonics hits us right were we work, in our cubicles and offices.

Next we proceed to three phase harmonics. While three phase harmonics is also a life/safety concern on a significantly lower scale, it has its own distinct characteristics in and of itself. These differences are important to understand since a common mistake is to confuse single phase issues with three phase issues.

It's tempting to suggest that the reader skip to the chapters that are more immediately applicable to a given site, situation, or area of concern. I don't recommend this, however. Experience has shown that even those comfortable with electrical concepts get the principles surrounding harmonics confused. For this reason, I recommend that each chapter be read in order.

Spend some time studying the graphs. Don't forget the time and magnitude scales. Try and translate what you see to your particular site. Imagine you are standing in front of an electrical panel and the waveform presented is coming from your meter. What does it mean to you in your world? How does it apply to your building?

After you have read the first few chapters, take some time to do some measuring. Try to duplicate some of what you have seen, as doing this will bring the book alive for you and put the concepts into the real world. As a matter of fact, one of the most valuable things you can do is to get your hands on a good meter, analyzer or oscilloscope, take a current probe, and go "play." Be careful to follow standard safety practices when you take measurements around live circuits, but explore the electrical environment around you. Look at your readings and the graphics in this book, and try to understand the relationship between voltage and current, and how pictures and readings of both relate. Be curious!

Find a peer you can talk to about the concepts presented here. Talk about problems you have encountered and how they relate to the chapter material. Finally, go to a class, seminar, or workshop. They are being given all over the country, and a phone call to a manufacturer , magazine, a trade show will eventually lead to information.

My sincere hope is that this book is easy to read and understand, and complete enough to arm you with everything you need to face the challenge of harmonics and to grow from there.

Mark Waller
February 2, 1994

1 Harmonics—What Are They?

When I was a teenager there seemed to be only one legitimate career to pursue—being in a rock-and-roll band. So without a single lesson, I mastered a fairly low level of guitar playing and launched myself toward fame and riches, strumming and plucking. All of us at that age wanted to emulate the Beatles or the Stones. Little did I know it at the time, but I was laying the foundation for the work I would do later in harmonic analysis.

I always marveled at skilled guitar players (which I never became). They seemed to be able to get a wide variety of sounds from the instrument without having to move their left hand up and down the strings. All they did was strum at a different place along the string, and different shades of tone would emerge. There was one particular technique that involved a light touch with the left hand that produced a very high pitched tone.

The Fundamental

If I plucked a string of my guitar in the center, the string would vibrate at the fundamental frequency. This is the lowest frequency at which the string is capable of vibrating. If we compare a guitar to a violin, for example, we see that the strings on a violin are considerably shorter than those on a guitar. Therefore, the fundamental frequency at which the violin string vibrates is considerably higher than that of a guitar (*Figure 1-1*).

The fundamental is the lowest frequency at which the string may vibrate, but this is a book about power, not rock and roll, and electricity oscillates rather than vibrates (*Figure 1-2*). Oscillation is a more precise term, whereas vibration brings to mind a mechanical process.

Utility power vibrates or oscillates at 60 Hz, and one vibratory or oscillatory cycle is completed in roughly 16-17 ms. The utility generators deliver sixty complete cycles every second, but because of the structure of the utility generation

Figure 1-1. *The fundamental frequency of the string is determined by the length of the string.*

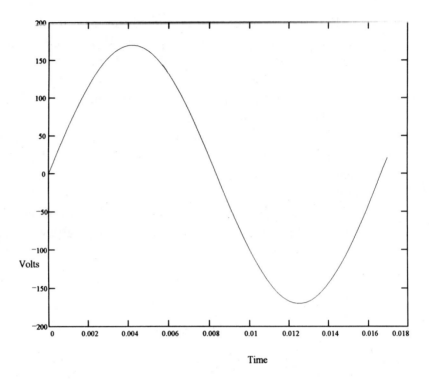

Figure 1-2. *The fundamental frequency of U.S. domestic power is 60Hz.*

system, it is impossible for us to get ten cycles per second. Also, utility generation is pretty solid in terms of frequency. The fundamental 60 cycle frequency seldom deviates from its fundamental frequency by more than a fraction of a Hertz.

If we were in France, it would be a different situation. The fundamental frequency of utility power in much of the world, including France, is 50 Hz, not 60 Hz. The utility customer in France gets only 50 cycles per second as opposed to 60 cycles per second in the U.S.A.

If we were in the military, it's entirely possible that the fundamental frequency of our power system might be 400 Hz, or we might have both 60 Hz and 400 Hz available. But whichever part of the system we look at, we would establish the fundamental frequency of power as being either 60 or 400 Hz.

Harmonics Defined

If we took the guitar and strummed a string near the end, we would find that the string vibrates at another frequency. If we could determine just what frequency that might be, we might find that the string is vibrating at a frequency that is three times the fundamental (*Figure 1-3*). We would intuitively know this since the pitch of the sound produced would be significantly higher than the pitch created when we strummed the string near the middle.

This, then, is the definition of harmonics: an integer multiple of the fundamental. Integer means a whole number (like 2), as opposed to a whole number and a fraction (like 2 1/2). If the string vibrates at a frequency that is three times the fundamental, we can say it is vibrating at the third harmonic.

In a 60 Hz power system, the third harmonic would be 180, or 3 x 60. *Table 1-1* shows the frequency of 60 Hz harmonics to the twentieth harmonic.

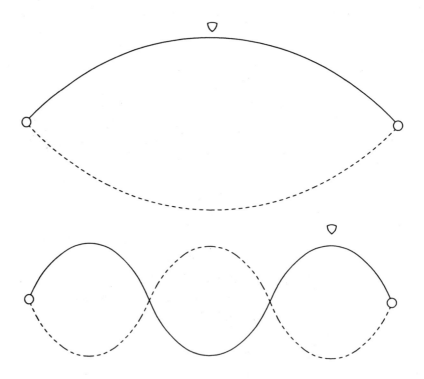

Figure 1-3. *This shows the string vibrating at three times the fundamental.*

If we strummed a guitar string near the end to produce the third harmonic vibration, and at the same time took a stop action photo of the string, it might look like the string shown in *Figure 1-4*. The shape of the string in vibratory flight is actually the sum of the fundamental and the third harmonic vibrations. And, while the pitch may seem higher to us, it has a richness that is pleasing to the ear. This richness is a result of the complexity of the various harmonics being produced plus the fundamental. Otherwise, the string would sound "tinny."

It is the rich mix of harmonics that gives the guitar its interesting sound. Other instruments, like the oboe, have entirely different harmonic complexities that make their musical signatures unique.

NAME	FREQUENCY—Hz
Fundamental	60
2nd	120
3rd	180
4th	240
5th	300
6th	360
7th	420
8th	480
9th	540
10th	600
11th	660
12th	720
13th	780
14th	840
15th	900
16th	960
17th	1020
18th	1080
19th	1140
20th	1200

Table 1-1. *This is a list of 60 Hz harmonics to the twentieth harmonic.*

Figure 1-4. *Here is the string vibrating at the sum of the fundamental and third harmonic.*

The Sine and Other Waves

Utility power comes to us in the form of sine waves, as shown in *Figure 1-1*. In fact, we get three sine waves, each 120° from the next, from the utility. The reason why we point out this sine wave distinction is because the study concerning power system harmonics is about sine waves, and how sine waves of various frequencies combine to form complex waveforms.

To understand this better, let's look at the mathematical formula for a sine wave. If you are not good at math, or if formulas are intimidating, hang in there. I believe you will find that this is easier than you think. The formula for a voltage sine wave is: $e = E \sin(2\pi ft.)$.

Little "e" is the voltage at any given instant. Little "t" is time. Big "E" is the peak voltage, and "f" stands for frequency. Of course, 2π is two times the irrational number pie, and "sin" is a trigonometric function.

Let's pick a value of 170v for E. That means the maximum voltage will be 170. In fact, that is true for the standard wall receptacle. The peak of 120v RMS (Root Mean Square) is about 170v. We would use a value of 60 for "f" since the fundamental frequency of utility power is 60 Hz. The value of "t" is something we will want to play with a little bit. For any given instant in time, we will get a different answer for "e." So what we want to do is solve the equation for the different values of "t."

A good series of values for "t" would be 0 -17 ms. in steps of tenths of milliseconds. If we plot the answer to these values of "e," we get the sine wave shown in *Figure 1-5*. This shape is said to be "sinusoidal." In other words, the shape of the series of functions varies as to the sine of the function.

We now have a fundamental sine wave. Let's modify the equation to plot the third harmonic. The first thing that must be modified is the value of "f." The frequency of the third harmonic is not 60 Hz; it's 180 Hz. We can substitute 180 for 60 for the value of "f," or we could just multiply "f" by 3. Remember, harmonics are integer multiples of the fundamental.

For a couple of reasons, I am going to modify the value of "E." First of all, I want the resulting waveform to be a little smaller than the fundamental so we can see it more easily. The other reason will become clear later. Let's multiply "E" by 1/3 so that the maximum voltage for the third harmonic will be only 1/3 of 170. *Figure 1-6* shows the fundamental and the third harmonic.

Let's see if we can mathematically duplicate the guitar string theory. We will do this by adding the formula for the fundamental to the formula for the third harmonic. *Figure 1-7* shows the fundamental, the third harmonic, and the sum of the two.

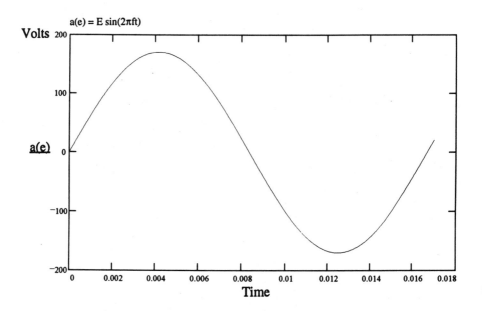

Figure 1-5. *The equation, timetable and plot of a sine wave.*

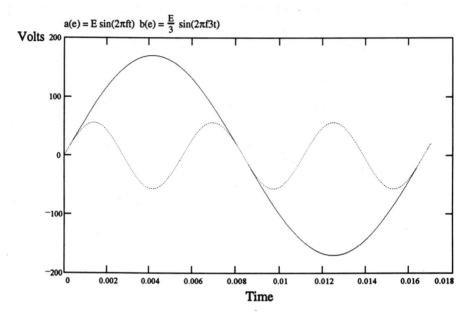

Figure 1-6. *The fundamental and the third harmonic.*

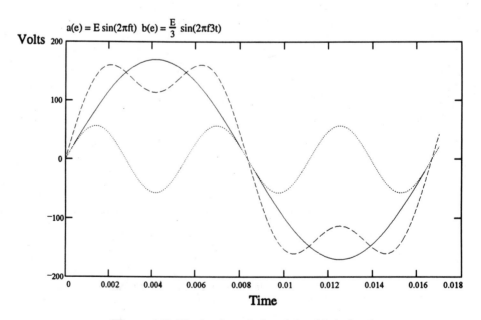

Figure 1-7. *The fundamental and the third plus the sum.*

But what if the third harmonic did not start at the same time as the fundamental? We call this concept "phasing." We can simulate this mathematically by changing the value of "t." The result in *Figure 1-8* is a lot different than the one in *Figure 1-7*. We will see something like this in a later chapter.

Let's go back to harmonics that are in phase with the fundamental. Let's take the sum in *Figure 1-7* and add it to the fifth harmonic and see what we get (*Figure 1-9*). The sum's shape looks familiar.

Now let's do it for the seventh harmonic (*Figure 1-10*), and the ninth harmonic (*Figure 1-11*). This looks like a square wave. In fact, the more odd numbered harmonics we add to the sum of the one before, the more perfect the square wave becomes. Now you see why I used the value of 1/3 for "E" earlier. The formula to create a square wave uses the harmonic number in the denominator of the fraction for each successive calculation, as well as the multiple for "f."

What's interesting and useful about this is that we can do the same thing backwards. Notice that all of the resultant wave forms that we generated are all non-sinusoidal. They all contain harmonics that make their shapes look "weird"—not like sine waves. But by doing the same process backwards, we can unravel the various harmonics and the fundamental, and we are right back to sine waves.

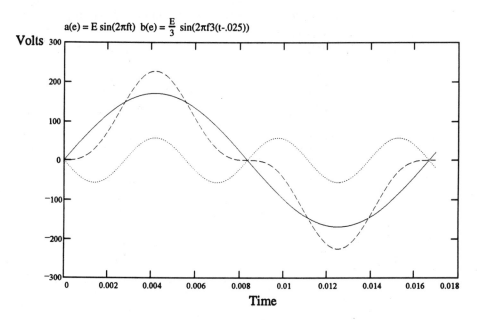

Figure 1-8. *The fundamental and phase shift of the third plus the sum.*

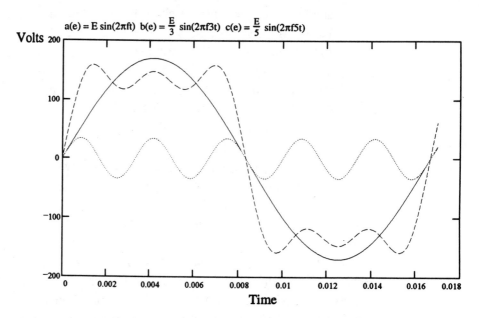

Figure 1-9. *The fundamental and the fifth plus the sum of the fundamental third and fifth.*

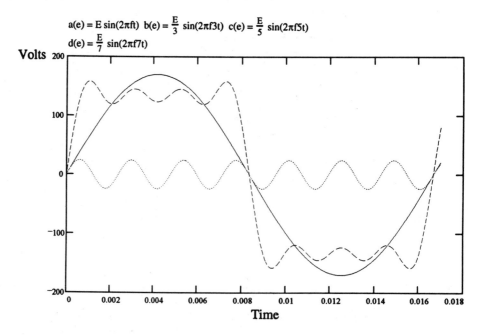

Figure 1-10. *The fundamental and seventh plus the sum of all and the seventh.*

It's just like a recipe for a waveform. What is the recipe for a square wave? You take some fundamental and add some of the third harmonic, and some of the fifth, and seventh, and ninth, and so on, and that's the recipe for a square wave. We will be dealing with these recipes throughout the book. To have a recipe that will give us everything we need to build (or unravel) any wave shape, we need to know three things; the harmonic, its phase position relative to the fundamental, and its magnitude relative to the fundamental. Science has given this process a name—**Harmonic Analysis**. (Somehow, it sounds more formal than **Cooking With Harmonics**.)

The bottom line to harmonic analysis is that non-sinusoidal repetitive wave shapes can be formed by a combination of sine waves at harmonic frequencies. Any distorted or discontinuitous wave shape can be described as sine wave components at various frequencies that are integer multiples of the fundamental. By decomposing any complex waveshape into a succession of individual harmonic sine waves, analysis becomes much easier.

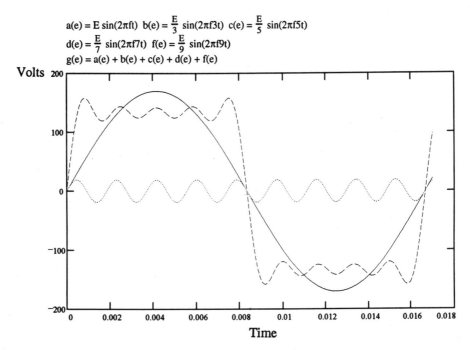

$$a(e) = E \sin(2\pi ft) \quad b(e) = \frac{E}{3} \sin(2\pi f3t) \quad c(e) = \frac{E}{5} \sin(2\pi f5t)$$

$$d(e) = \frac{E}{7} \sin(2\pi f7t) \quad f(e) = \frac{E}{9} \sin(2\pi f9t)$$

$$g(e) = a(e) + b(e) + c(e) + d(e) + f(e)$$

Figure 1-11. *The fundamental and ninth plus the sum of all and the ninth.*

Harmonic Analysis

In 1822, the French mathematician Jean Baptiste Joseph Fourier (1768-1830) theorized that any continuous function repetitive in an interval of time could be represented by the summation of a fundamental sine wave with a series of higher order harmonic components at frequencies which are integer multiples of the fundamental frequency. Today we call this a Fourier series. Harmonic analysis is the process of computing the magnitudes and phases of the fundamental and higher order harmonics of the periodic waveform. The resulting series of numbers establishes a relationship between the time-based function and that same function in the frequency domain.

Today, we use a modified version of Fourier's transform called fast Fourier transform. These are basically algorithms that are the computational basis for modern spectral and harmonic analyzers. It is not our purpose to delve deeply into Fourier's calculus; there are many good books on the subject. The higher math and deep theory behind harmonics are not the purpose of this book, but hopefully this chapter has supplied you with enough background to understand what follows.

2 Non-linear Loads

Load is a term commonly used to describe any device that draws current from the power source. A linear load would be one which draws current in sine waves. Or, a linear load draws current in step, proportional to the voltage waveform (*Figure 2-1*). A non-linear load is one that draws current in a non-sinusoidal fashion, even when the voltage is a perfect sine wave (*Figure 2-2*). One thing is certain; whether the current waveform is distorted or not is strictly a function of the

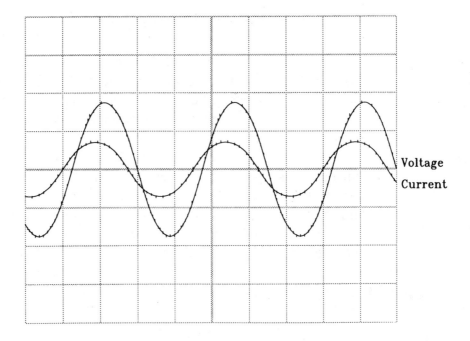

Figure 2-1. *This figure shows how difficult it is to find a pure sine wave in the real world. Even though there is an obvious phase shift between current and voltage, it is linear compared to Figure 2-2.* (Adapted from Fluke ScopeMeter)

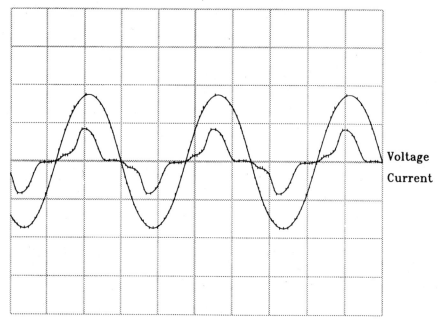

Figure 2-2. *Sine wave voltage and non-linear current.*

load connected to the power source. It is not possible (contrary to popular opinion) for the utility to send distorted current to the load. The source may have a distorted voltage waveform, but the load current is normally a function of the load device and how it wants to draw current. Distorted voltage, however, will result in non-sinusoidal current.

We call this non-linearity distortion. Waveform distortion is not a new phenomenon and keeping it to an acceptable minimum has been a goal of power engineers since the early days of alternating current. One reason for this concern stems from the fact that the power system has been designed to handle 60 Hz power. Waveform distortion has high frequency components which cause significant heating of conductors, transformers, and other power components.

Skin and Other Effects

A conductor's resistance is not the same for direct current as it is for alternating current, and as the frequency of the alternating current increases, so does the resistance. This is known as the "skin effect" (*Figure 2-3*). What happens with AC is that current is forced to flow toward the outer parts of the conductor. This

Current flow at 60Hz

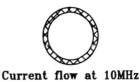
Current flow at 10MHz

Figure 2-3. *Skin effect.*

effectively decreases the cross-sectional area of the conductor, and as a result, resistance increases.

At low audio frequencies, the skin effect is insignificant, but at radio frequencies above 1 MHz, the skin effect is so dramatic that nearly all of the current flows within a few thousandths of an inch of the surface. As a matter of fact, at radio frequencies, a conductor of thin tubing is just as effective as a solid wire. We don't generally think of harmonic frequencies as being radio frequencies, but harmonic heating will increase the resistance of any metallic conductor, thereby adding to the problem.

The effects of higher power frequencies don't stop with conductors, bus bars, and feeders. Breakers are designed to open on temperature, unless they include a magnetic trip as well. Certainly, they are overcurrent devices, but it is the heating of the breaker due to the current that makes the breaker trip. Breakers are designed to use the connected conductor as a heat sink to radiate ambient energy away from the thermal tripping element. If the wire is already warm from the flow of harmonic currents, it's not much of a heat sink. In fact, this process will lower the trip point of the breaker, and has been a frequent source of nuisance tripping of breakers when the RMS current was actually under the rating of the breaker.

Transformers

When AC flows through the coil of a transformer wound on an iron or steel core, current is induced in the core itself. These currents are called eddy currents. They represent power loss since they flow through the core and generate heat. At higher frequencies eddy current losses increase. An even bigger factor involves eddy current losses in the windings themselves, which limit transformer capacity.

Another type of loss is called hysteresis. Hysteresis losses are due to the energy that must be used to change the magnetic state of cores and conductors. As frequency increases, hysteresis losses increase. We'll discuss this later when we look at K-rated transformers.

The Power Distribution System

Heating, in general, is not the only problem created by non-linear loads. Additional problems are created when we begin to connect these loads to the building distribution system. Loads can interact with other loads, and load currents may combine in unexpected ways, or stray circuits can be unintentionally set up using the non-linear load or loads as key elements in the setup. All of these topics will be covered in later chapters. But suffice it to say, the majority (if not all) of these effects are unplanned, by both utility engineers and building electrical design engineers.

Non-linear Load Elements

Something has changed in the last 10 - 20 years in power electronics. Prior to that time, the majority of electrical loads were of a type depicted in *Figure 2-4*. Notice that the load circuit components are made up of a combination of resistive, inductive, and capacitive elements. If the load is largely capacitive or inductive, then the power factor of the load will vary from unity. While this might be a concern, the load current is still a sine wave.

With the advent of power semiconductors, all of that changed. It is still possible to have "bad" power factor from capacitive or inductive loads, but power semiconductors, when coupled with resistive, capacitive, and inductive circuit elements, create non-linear load currents (*Figure 2-5*).

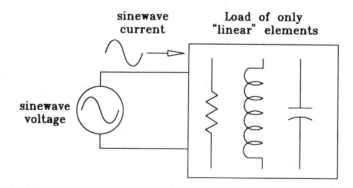

Figure 2-4. *Linear load elements. Note that all indicators are not linear.*
The core will make a difference,

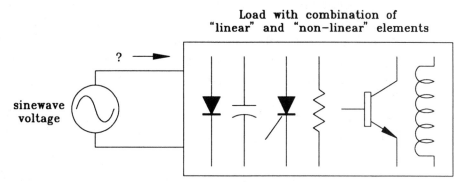

Figure 2-5. *Non-linear load elements.*

A point should be made here about a type of non-linear load that we'll be talking about quite a bit—the switching or switch-mode power supply. Years ago, before the advent of the personal computer, most radios, TVs, and desktop terminals used what has been called a linear power supply. This power supply had a characteristic up-front 60 Hz transformer, which made it bulky and heavy. Today, virtually every type of electronic device, from VCRs to PCs, uses what's called a switching or switch-mode power supply. Gone is the big transformer. Switchers are small and lightweight. But, as we will see, they are among the biggest contributors to the problem of single phase harmonics. (Linear supplies were, in many cases, just as non-linear in current draw as the modern switcher. The issue is not that the switcher is worse—it's that there are so many of them!)

The Harmonic Universe is Expanding

There has been a significant proliferation of types and numbers of non-linear loads in recent years. Ironically enough, the very device that is the most non-linear may be the most susceptible to harmonic distortion. Consider for a moment the increase in microprocessor-based equipment. The typical high-rise office tower built in the 1970s had few, if any, of these kinds of loads. Today, there may be several hundred per floor.

It's not just computers. Just take a walk through any facility. It's hard to find any device that does not use this technology, including clocks, radios, copiers, and PC-type equipment. The Electrical Power Research Institute estimates that 15% of the load on the nation's grid is electronic in nature, and they claim it will move up to 50% within ten years.

Certainly advances in electrotechnology and computing are driving this expansion, but another, more insidious driver of the growth in harmonic loads has emerged. The technologies available to accomplish this are all power converters of one type or another with powerful financial paybacks for installation and application. The problem is that these are all harmonic generators and they are proliferating like stars in the universe.

Harmonics vs. Transients

Here is an area where there is a lot of confusion. Harmonics are not transients. A transient, as defined by the *IEEE Emerald Book* is "a subcycle disturbance in the AC waveform that is evidenced by a sharp brief discontinuity of the waveform." The use of the word "transient," by definition, indicates the time nature of the event—transients are random or separated by a wide space of time.

Harmonic distortion, on the other hand, is steady state, repeating cycle after cycle. It can come and go, but it is not "subcycle" in nature.

Harmonics doesn't mean grounding, surges or spikes, or what happens when the power fails. There used to be one term commonly used by the uninformed to describe every conceivable power quality problem—"surge." The facilities manager who peers over the lighted candle in his pitch dark office and says, "We must have had a surge," probably means to say "outage." And today, when the computer crashes because the grounding violates the National Electrical Code, he is likely to say, "We must be having harmonics" (when what he should say is, "We need to get our act together!").

Voltage, Current and Impedance

In this section, we assume that the power source is capable of producing sinusoidal voltage. There are some sources that do produce distorted output, even lightly loaded—static UPSs come to mind. But if we look at the typical transformer given a sine wave input, you will get a sine wave on its output until an electrical load is connected to it. If that load has a linear current draw, the output voltage waveform will be unaffected.

If, however, the load current is non-linear, the output voltage waveform may or may not become distorted. The common element that ties current to voltage in the production of harmonic distortion is impedance (*Figure 2-6* shows a simplified diagram of transformer impedance). The internal impedance is the geometric

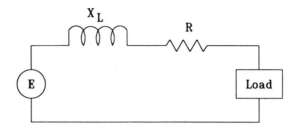

Figure 2-6. *Transformer impedance model.*

sum of the transformer's resistance and inductive reactance (the opposition of current flow from the windings or inductance in the transformer) at the frequency for which the device was designed.

Voltage distortion is a function of the impedance of the source and the way that current is drawn through that impedance. Power source impedance is equal to the change in voltage produced by and incremental change in current: $Z = \Delta E / \Delta I$. Notice in *Figure 2-6* that X_L and R are in series with the load, and the load current will create a voltage drop across this impedance. The formula for X_L is $X_L = 2\pi fL$. The "f" in the formula stands for frequency. Obviously, inductive reactance will change directly with frequency. This means that at harmonic frequencies, the power source impedance is greater than at 60 Hz. The term for this characteristic is **forward transfer impedance**.

From the perspective of the load, this is called **output impedance**. The source's **output impedance** governs what happens to the voltage when incremental changes in current are drawn. Let's rearrange our formula for impedance and look at it from a voltage drop point of view: $\Delta E = Z \times \Delta I$. For a given Z, the change in current will produce a corresponding drop or increase in voltage. *Figure 2-7* shows a sinusoidal current and corresponding voltage waveform, and *Figure 2-8* shows a non-linear current and corresponding voltage waveform.

In *Figure 2-7*, the sinusoidal load current changes relatively slowly, and the voltage waveform remains undistorted. Meanwhile, *Figure 2-8* shows a dramatic step load change and a resulting "flat topping" of the voltage waveform. This is exactly what we might have expected looking at the formula $\Delta E = Z \times \Delta I$.

Voltage distortion is a function of loading, and voltage harmonics are caused by current harmonics. The forward transfer impedance is dynamic depending on the harmonic content of the load current. The load sees any voltage drop due to non-linear load current as high output impedance on the part of the source at the harmonic frequencies of interest.

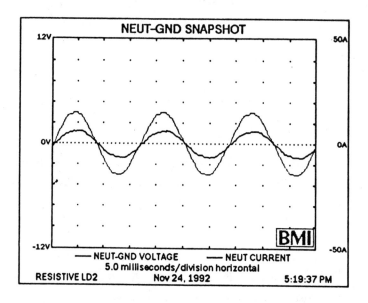

Figure 2-7. *The linear nature of the current does not affect the voltage waveform.*

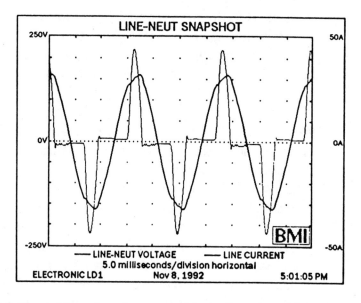

Figure 2-8. *The sudden pulse of current results in distortion of the voltage waveform*
(ΔE = ZΔ x I).

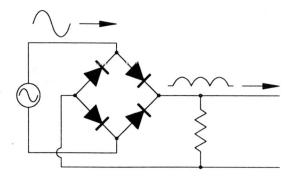

Figure 2-9. *Current flow through the diode bridge is nearly linear when the load is resistive.*

Non-linear Current—Why?

The current signature shown in *Figure 2-8* is probably familiar. It is the current signature of a switching power supply, the kind found in almost every single phase electronic device in the world. But why does this switcher draw current in short pulses and not in sine waves?

To understand the answer to this, we must look at the up-front circuit components of the power supply and how current flows through them. *Figure 2-9* shows a full wave bridge rectifier circuit. During the positive half cycle, two of the diodes in the bridge conduct. During the negative half cycle, the other pair of diodes conduct. Assuming the load is purely resistive, the input sine waveshape would be converted into ripple DC on the output of the bridge, and the bridge conduction would occur during the entire 360° of the sine wave.

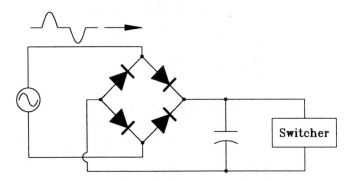

Figure 2-10. *When the bridge is followed by a capacitor, current flows in pulses.*

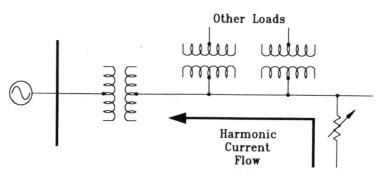

Figure 2-11. *Harmonic current flows from the non-linear load toward the utility source.*

But the load elements of a switcher are not purely resistive. In fact, the next and most important circuit element in a switch-mode power supply is a rather large capacitor. This electrolytic capacitor is essential in providing a steady source of current for the switch. A characteristic of this capacitor is that it will only draw current when the rectified voltage across its terminal exceeds its charged voltage.

As *Figure 2-10* shows, this condition only exists for a few degrees of each half cycle, and only at the peak of the voltage sine wave, since this is when the input voltage exceeds the charged voltage of the capacitor. Therefore, diode conduction occurs in short pulses, and large amounts of current flow in a non-linear fashion.

This is only one of the many non-linear relationships we will explore throughout the book. Now that we have background knowledge of what harmonics are and what causes them, it is time to analyze what harmonics can do in the power system. We will start with PCs and lighting ballasts, and fully explore the single phase world before we move on to three phase harmonic issues.

The Paradox of Harmonic Current

Before we move on, however, we need to orient our thinking to harmonic current. In one important way, it presents us with a paradox. The utility company can be assumed to be a nearly unlimited source of pure sine wave voltage, but at the same time, we know that the power system inside a building contains non-linear or non-sinusoidal current. As that harmonic current passes through the distribution system, losses at each harmonic frequency are produced, but at the utility's generators, only power at the fundamental frequency is produced. So what happens to the power dissipated inside the building at harmonic frequencies?

Basic physics tells us that energy absorbed in the system at each frequency must equal the energy pumped into the system. Since the utility is a source of power at the fundamental, the non-linear loads must be the "source" of power at the harmonic frequencies. Since the utility generators are supplying energy at the fundamental, energy at any other frequency must be coming from non-linear loads.

Figure 2-11 shows the flow of harmonic current. A switching power supply then can be seen as a non-linear shunt device that itself is a "generator" of non-linear current at frequencies above the fundamental. The non-linear load converts power from one frequency to other frequencies. Since the utility is the lowest impedance path for those harmonic currents, they can be conceptualized as flowing toward the utility source. It should be remembered, however, that all current, whether it is non-linear or linear, flows in a loop between the load and the source. In other words, current always flows in circuits, and the source still produces the current from which the load derives its harmonic current.

3 Multiple PCs and Single Phase Harmonics

A number of years ago, I wrote an article for *Network World* called "Multiple PCs—A New Fire Hazard." Not long after the article came out, I received a phone call from a fireman in a town near San Diego who was also the data processing manager for the fire department.

He said that he had started reading the article late one Sunday evening, and normally would have gone to bed rather than finish it except something caught his eye. As he read further, his interest grew. Finally, he slammed down the magazine and exclaimed, "That's what burned down our accounting department!"

During our conversation, he told me that after the fire, investigators had traced the problem to a hot neutral conductor, but they could not figure out why a neutral would be hot enough to start a fire.

In this chapter, we are going to see what happened in this case and in many other cases around the country. This problem is certainly not restricted to PCs. Not too long ago, I received a frantic phone call from a man who was afraid he was going to have a transformer fire, which we will discuss in a later chapter. I arrived to do a harmonic analysis on the facility only to discover that the transformer supported hundreds of VCRs, all of which were duplicating video tapes. (I can't tell you what movie was being duplicated, but I was able to determine that adult videos produce the same level of harmonic distortion as any other tape in a VCR. I wonder if I should notify the IEEE.)

The Harmonic Analysis

Figure 3-1 shows the the current drawn by many switching power supplies inside PCs, and *Figure 3-2* shows the current signature of dozens of VCRs. Notice the similarities between the two—both use diode/capacitor inputs.

Let's take one of these current waveforms and do a harmonic analysis and see what we get. *Figure 3-3* shows the analysis that came out of the BMI 3030 that

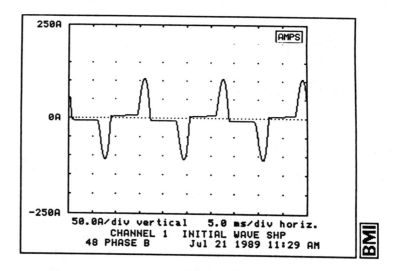

Figure 3-1. *The current waveform of switching power supplies.*

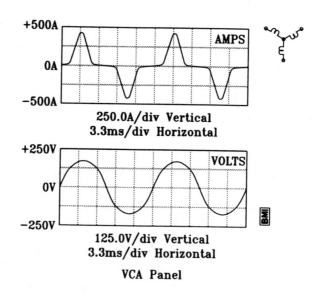

Figure 3-2. *The current signature of dozens of VCRs.*

		Phase A Current Spectrum	Mar 09 1992 (Mon) 10:59:30 AM
Fundamental amps:	181.4 rms
Fundamental freq:	60.0 Hz

HARM	PCT	SINE PHASE	HARM	PCT	SINE PHASE
FUND	100.0%	-12°	2nd	0.2%	22°
3rd	50.0%	151°	4th	0.3%	-157°
5th	15.6%	-66°	6th	0.3%	-7°
7th	5.1%	14°	8th	0.1%	140°
9th	2.4%	125°	10th		
11th	0.8%	178°	12th		
13th	1.0%	-74°	14th		
15th	0.5%	4°	16th		
17th	0.7%	116°	18th		
19th	0.4%	-175°	20th		
21st	0.4%	-74°	22nd		
23rd	0.4%	-12°	24th		
25th	0.3%	84°	26th		
27th	0.3%	152°	28th		
29th	0.2%	-123°	30th		
31st	0.2%	-32°	32nd		
33rd	0.1%	43°	34th		
35th	0.1%	143°	36th		
37th			38th		
39th			40th		
41st	0.1%	47°	42nd		
43rd			44th		
45th	0.1%	-128°	46th		
47th			48th		
49th	0.1%	39°	50th		
ODD	52.7%		**EVEN**	0.5%	

Figure 3-3. *Harmonic analysis of the wave shape in Figure 3-2.*

I used on site. But let's see if all of these numbers really mean what they say. Let's try to construct the waveform mathematically.

In *Figure 3-4*, we took the fundamental and the next two largest harmonics to see if they would add up to anything like the current waveform in *Figure 3-2*. Notice the parts of the equations that correspond to the numbers in the analysis.

The first equation is that of the fundamental. We have modified it slightly by moving the phase position in a negative direction 12°. Next comes the third harmonic. We modify the equation by multiplying E by .5, since the analysis shows that the third harmonic is 50% of the fundamental. Then we multiply the angle α by 3 to increase the frequency to the third harmonic. Then we add 151° to the phase position, and we go through the same process with the fifth harmonic. We multiply E by .156, α by 5, and subtract 66° from the phase position.

Harmonic analysis seems to work! There are a lot of other harmonic components listed in the analysis, but by using just the three largest components, we have a waveform that looks very much like the one in *Figure 3-2*.

Once, I was asked to analyze all of the single phase electronic loads in a particular building. *Figure 3-5* shows a sample of these loads, from a variety of PCs, file servers, and similar types of equipment. They all have the pulse current signatures that characterize PCs.

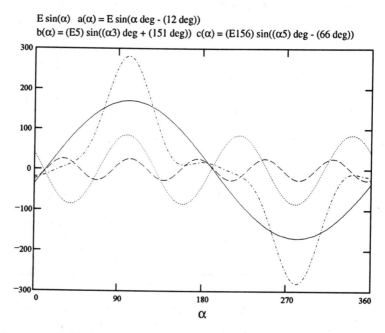

Figure 3-4. *Mathematical reconstruction of the waveform in Figure 3-2.*

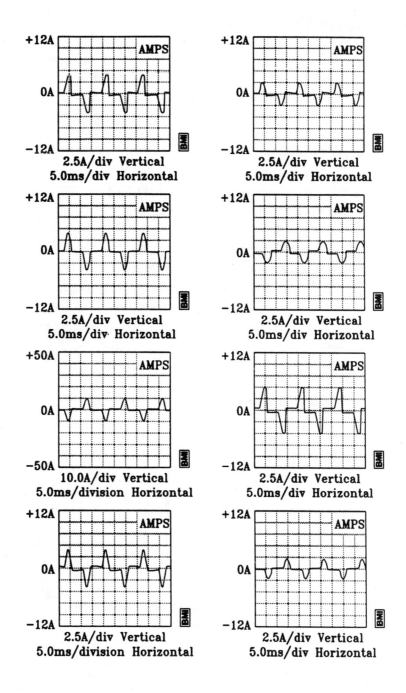

Figure 3-5. *A sample of electronic loads. All have similar current waveforms.*

Single Phase Distribution

When you walk through a modern office building, what kinds of single phase loads do you see? The trend is to condominiumize the work space. It's not unusual to find a PC and at least one other type of work station along with associated printers and peripheral devices. In fact, nearly every steady state load in the work area may be a switching power supply-type load! That includes copiers and laser printers.

Copiers and laser printers draw current in three distinct ways. First, as they idle along, they draw current just like a PC (*Figure 3-6*). They have a small switcher which powers the electronics. Second, every so often (10 - 30 seconds), the drum heater turns on. This is a very linear (resistive) load, so the waveform looks sinusoidal. Third, they draw current when they are actually printing. The waveform varies, but it's fairly linear with some distortion. As a matter of fact, about the only steady state load in the office area that is not badly distorted is the space heater that is found tucked under the desk of many workers.

That being the case, let's look at the typical single phase distribution system and see how it's supposed to work. *Figure 3-7* shows an extremely simplified diagram of the typical office area that is found in most commercial buildings. Notice that the three phase conductors from the Delta/Wye, 480/208Y120 transformer pass through the distribution transformer and go out to the single phase loads.

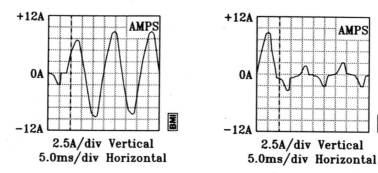

Figure 3-6. *When a laser printer idles, we see the signature of a switching power supply. When its drum heater cycles on, a large step load to sine wave current occurs.*

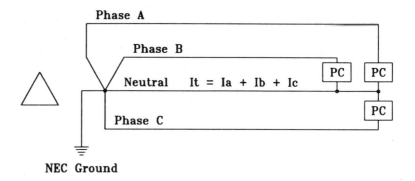

Figure 3-7. *A simplified single phase distribution diagram.*

There is one neutral conductor for all three phases. Therefore, the load currents combine in a common neutral conductor. (This makes a lot of sense, at least it used to.) Let's pretend that all of the loads connected to the three phases are linear loads. In other words, all three current waveforms look like pure sine waves. *Figure 3-6* shows three phase current waves, each 120° from one another. This is the way three phase power is delivered from the utility. If we geometrically add these three phase currents, all three phases cancel in the common neutral, and the result is a straight line through zero.

For many years, the National Electrical Code allowed for this condition, and a reduction in the neutral conductor ampacity was permitted. In some circumstances where #10 phase conductors were used, it is not uncommon to find #12 neutral conductors. This condition is more prevalent in older buildings and in older partition furniture.

The Dreaded Third Harmonic

As we have seen, the typical switching power supply current waveform contains many harmonics (*Figure 3-3*). The bulk of the harmonic currents can be described as the third harmonic or 180 Hz. Let's take the same equations we used to build the three phase model in *Figure 3-8* and use them to see what happens to the third harmonic.

The first thing we have to do is to plot the third harmonic of phase A. To convert the equation to the third harmonic, we must first multiply α by 3. Over the

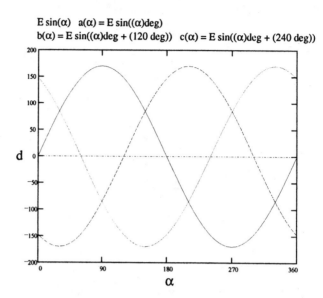

Figure 3-8. *Three phase currents (A,B,C) 120° from one another cancel in the neutral. The sum of the three, D, is 0.*

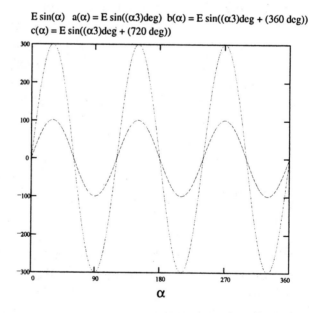

Figure 3-9. *Three phase third harmonics add in the neutral. The smaller waveform is actually three smaller waves on top of each other. The larger waveform is the sum of those three.*

same time frame, roughly 16 - 17 ms. or 360°, we will get three waveforms instead of one, as in 60 Hz.

Next we will plot the third harmonic of phase B. This will start 120° times 3 later, or at 360°. Plotting the third harmonic of phase C starts at 3 times 240°, or at 720°. Notice that these phase positions, 360 and 720, are divisible by 360.

There seems to be only one waveform plotted in *Figure 3-9*, but look at the magnitude. Believe it or not, there are three waves plotted. They are right on top of one another (zero sequenced). The third harmonic from each phase crosses the zero line at the same time or phase position, and the third harmonic adds in a common neutral conductor, but it's not just the third harmonic that does this.

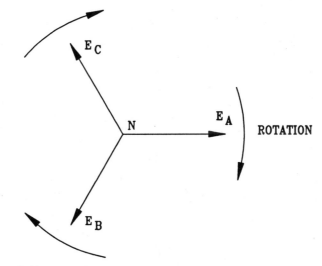

Figure 3-10. *Phasor diagram of positively sequenced phases (A,B,C).*

Sequencing

In a three phase power system, the current at the fundamental frequency has a phasor rotation (*Figure 3-10*). In an induction motor, this phasor rotation produces a corresponding magnetic field that rotates in the same direction.

Harmonic currents do not always produce a rotating field that is in sequence with the fundamental—the consecutive harmonic waveforms do not always follow the same order as the fundamental. *Figure 3-11* shows a phasor diagram of a "negatively sequenced" harmonic. Notice that the letters are no longer in alphabetical order. The rotating field produced by a negatively sequenced harmonic is in opposition to that produced by the fundamental. You may have experienced

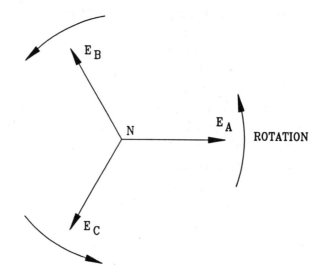

Figure 3-11. *Phasors for negative sequenced phases (A,C,B).*

the phenomenon of connecting a three phase motor incorrectly and watching it run backwards. Imagine the heating effects the presence of negatively sequenced harmonics have on the motor that is connected to run on positively sequenced fundamental. The motor must overcome the effect of negative torque.

There are harmonics that have the same phasor rotation as the fundamental. These are called "positively sequenced." And, of course, there are those that are zero sequenced, like the third harmonic. In fact, the third and odd multiples of the third are all zero sequenced. They are known as triplens, or triplen harmonics. A phasor diagram of a zero sequenced harmonic is shown in *Figure 3-12*. Obviously, no rotating field will be produced by triplen harmonics. *Table 3-1* shows a schedule of a number of harmonics and their sequence relationships.

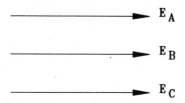

Figure 3-12. *Phasors of zero sequenced phases.*

Harmonic	Frequency	Sequence Network
1	60	+
2	120	-
3	180	0
4	240	+
5	300	-
6	360	0
7	420	+
8	480	-
9	540	0
10	600	+

Table 3-1. *Harmonics and sequence relationships.*

So, How Much Current?

If we refer back to *Figure 3-9*, we will notice that the peak was set at 100, but by the time all three phases of the third harmonic were added together, the sum was three times as large. The maximum practical limit for neutral current from triplen harmonics is $1.73 \cdot \sqrt{3}$ times the phase current.

In practice, however, it rarely gets that high. *Table 3-2* shows the neutral current measured in a high-rise building. These floors support any number of single phase electronic loads. Note that the typical 480/208Y120 transformer and panel will have anywhere from 130% to 225% of the current in the largest loaded phase. This current is made up of the third and any unbalanced fundamental or other harmonic current.

Early in the exploration of this issue, a landmark study was conducted by James Moravek and Edward Lethert. Their survey of neutral current in sixty-six different sites confirms our experience. Neutrals supporting computer loads exhibit an average neutral to phase current ratio of about 149%.

Figure 3-13 shows typical neutral currents at three phase panels supporting single phase electronic loads. Notice that the horizontal axis confirms that these are indeed 180 Hz current. These waveforms, or something very near them, are always present where there are these types of loads.

Floor	Phase A	Phase B	Phase C	Neutral
13th Amps	11.8	10.2	8.1	23.7
19th Amps	40.5	32.0	13.6	44.6
40th Amps	45.1	40.5	51.8	67.9
43rd Amps	59.9	79	66.9	77.9
44th Amps	30.2	62.6	51.7	56.3
45th Amps	32.7	26	9.5	47
46th Amps	34.4	43.2	57.6	50
47th Amps	50.5	52.2	103.3	95.2
48th Amps	49.5	46.1	48.6	81.6

Table 3-2. *This table shows the phase and neutral currents in some of the floors of one high-rise building in downtown Los Angeles.*

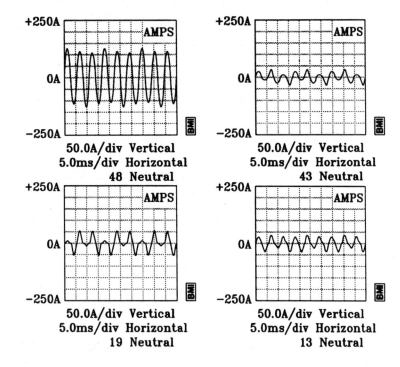

Figure 3-13. *These printouts show some of the neutrals measured in the high-rise. Notice that in all cases the waveform repeats three times in about 15 ms. This means we are looking at 180 Hz current or the effect of the additive third harmonic flowing in the neutral.*

Let's Build a Building Fire!

How does all of this add up? Let's see by way of a fictitious building. In the building, we will assume that we are looking at a distribution panel servicing the customer service department of a local utility. Branch circuit phase conductors utilize a #10 black wire, which is typical of many facilities.

QUIZ # 1: What is the ampacity of a #10 wire typically found in an office area?
Answer: 30 amps.

This all depends on a number of factors, but we are heading somewhere here, and it is the final point that is important. Those of you who are code experts, just follow this for a moment and suspend your judgements.

The neutral conductors are #12s, permitted by code and by virtue of winning the lowest bid for electrical work. They are the common return path for current flowing from three black or phase conductors. If we go to the panel and count forty-two phase conductors, we will find only fourteen white wires. This means that for every three phase conductors there is one neutral conductor—the theory being that the current would be sinusoidal and much of it would cancel in the neutral.

QUIZ #2: What is the ampacity of the typical #12 wire?
Answer: 25 amps.

QUIZ #3: What breaker size will we likely find?
Answer: 20 amp breakers.

We have #10 phase conductors with 20 amp breakers. We have #12 neutrals, but . . .

QUIZ #4: What is the allowable continuous loading on our 20 amp circuits?
Answer: 80%, or 16 amps.

For the sake of argument, let's assume that we have our circuits loaded with about four PCs and associated hardware so that we have four workstations on each circuit, each drawing 16 amp.

Let's be conservative and assume that the neutral to phase current ratio is about 1.5.

QUIZ #5: What is the neutral current?
Answer: 16 x 150%, or about 24 amps.

It looks like we are dangerously close to exceeding the ampacity of the neutral. But wait! We used a conservative 1.5 neutral to phase current ratio. It really might be closer to 2.0, in which case our neutral current would be nearly 30 amps!

QUIZ #6: How many more PCs can we plug in before we burn down the building?
Answer: We had better do a harmonic analysis right now and find out!

Remember, there is no breaker on the neutral conductor. A fire can start long before a overcurrent protection device is activated. The National Electrical Code states that where more than three current-carrying conductors are in a raceway or cable, further derating is required. The fact that harmonics are present means that the neutral conductor must be considered a current-carrying conductor.

Areas of Concern

We have already hinted that any work area that supports a lot of PCs (ie: switch-mode power supplies) is a potential disaster. This not only includes the office area, but the factory floor as well. PLCs (program logic controllers) are nothing more than industrial versions of PCs. CAD/CAM areas should also be watched.

Partition furniture is one other thing to be aware of. Some manufacturers have identified harmonics as a problem, and the brand new models are designed accordingly. However, older furniture is not. Also, be on the lookout for surge strips plugged into surge strips. These multi-outlet strips are UL listed as "temporary power taps," which means just that—they are temporary. Many municipalities take a dim view of them as a potential fire hazard, and harmonics is just one of the problems they are concerned about.

4 Lighting Ballasts and Harmonics

Few of us have ever really stopped to take stock of what happened to the world we live in as a result of a memorable event that took place in 1973. The event was the oil crisis, and it extended in one form or another until about 1979. Many things about our lives changed during those years, and the drive to make future changes started during those years. It was the practical dawn of the move toward electrical energy conservation.

The result was a number of energy saving technologies that would change the face of electrical power quality for a generation. These technologies were energy saving lighting ballasts, electronic lighting ballasts, adjustable speed motor drives (now more precisely known as variable frequency drives), microprocessor-controlled energy management systems, and a variety of other energy efficient products using electrotechnology.

Then along came the 1980s and a renewed interest in the environment. The concern for clean air created a move away from fossil fuel-based systems toward electrotechnologies. In the meantime, utilities and regulatory agencies were looking with concern at the ever growing need for generating facilities which fit, ironically, into the entire environmental scenario.

As a result of a variety of economic incentives, utilities have become active in pushing programs and priorities that encourage energy conservation, as well as the purchase of energy efficient electrotechnologies. The other single biggest player in this movement is government, at all levels. Legislation and agency mandates from federal and state regulatory agencies have added to the momentum.

Various energy legislations have required the production and application of energy efficient fluorescent lamp ballasts, for example. As of January 1, 1990, ballast manufacturers were required to produce only energy efficient ballasts under certain circumstances. Then, as of April 1, 1990, they were allowed to sell only the energy efficient versions of those ballasts. Furthermore, by the following year, only energy efficient versions of certain models were allowed to be installed.

Then came the Energy Policy Act of 1992, which established minimum efficiency standards and labelling requirements for electric motors, commercial heating and cooling systems, fluorescent lighting, and other equipment, and outlawed most of the fluorescent lamp types in common use.

This chapter is not meant to be a reference source on all of the various laws and regulations that are pushing toward this huge overhaul in lighting technology. Suffice it to say, the move is on in a big way, and ballast manufacturers are among the fastest growing business entities in the country.

This push to update lighting makes a lot of sense since lighting accounts for 40 - 50% of the total energy use by commercial and industrial utility customers. In addition, lighting is the single largest component of peak demand for any electrical utility. By reducing this load, expensive and potentially polluting generating plants can be deferred. Every silver lining has a cloud, and energy efficient ballasts are no exception. Harmonics are a concern, and must be understood and considered when applying ballast technology.

The Lighting Short Story

A fluorescent lamp consists of a glass tube filled with argon gas and a small amount of mercury. The inside of the tube is coated with phosphors. It is the phosphor coating's job to turn ultraviolet light into visible light. Specially coated tungsten electrodes are located at each end of the tube, and when a voltage is applied across the electrodes, an arc is created through the mercury vapor. This arc produces the ultraviolet light that, when absorbed by the phosphors, produces visible light.

It is the job of the ballast to provide the initial voltage surge to initiate the arc. Once the arc path has been established, the ballast must limit the current going through the lamp arc, which acts similar to a short circuit which, without regulation, would burn up the lamp. The other job of the ballast is to heat electrodes and to keep them heated.

The traditional ballast is known as a magnetic ballast. This is due to the design of the unit. Magnetic ballasts use wire wound around a laminated steel core to form transformers and inductors. Energy-saver magnetic ballasts are similar to traditional magnetic ballasts except that higher quality materials are used so that core losses and wire resistance losses are minimized.

Figure 4-1 shows the current draw of one such magnetic core ballast. Intuitively, we can see that there is a great deal of third harmonic present. In fact, there

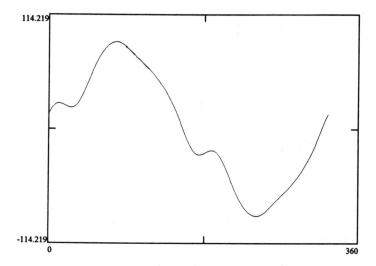

Figure 4-1. *The current waveform of a magnetic core ballast.*

is 13.5% third harmonic distortion, and there is an additional 11.2% of fifth harmonic. The overall total harmonic distortion (THD) is 18%. This contrasts sharply with the 100% levels that we saw with PC power supplies.

Why Electronics?

In a word? Efficiency! But there is more to the story than that. At 60 Hz, which is the frequency of operation of magnetic ballasts, there is a resonance condition created with the phosphorus molecules. In order to produce visible light, this resonance must be overcome. This uses energy, about 30% of the power consumed by the light. If we can operate the fixture at some other frequency, we can avoid this condition. This is where electronics comes in.

Figure 4-2 shows one possible electronic ballast configuration used to operate a metal halide fixture. Notice the input diode bridge. Although the circuitry is different, the basic electronics is similar to a switching power supply. What happens is that the incoming 60 Hz power is chopped up into power that is delivered at 20 kHz. This avoids the resonance problem and delivers significantly more efficiency. Typical operating frequencies for electronic ballasts range from 20 - 60 kHz. In lighting terms, this results in a better lamp lumens per watt ratio (LPW).

The higher the frequency, the more phosphor excitation, which produces more light output for a given input power level.

Other benefits accrue as well. Electronic ballasts have a lower operating temperature than magnetic ballasts. This means lower thermal losses and a better ambient temperature for the lamp itself. This also translates into lower air conditioning loads. In addition, a 60 Hz transformer can be a noisy device due to the vibration of the core laminates at 60 Hz. We all know the distinctive buzz that is sometimes heard when the lights are turned on. Electronic ballasts result in significantly less audible noise. Perceived light flicker is also eliminated using electronic ballasts. Anyone who wears contact lenses, especially, can be irritated by flicker. Over a period of time, task lighting flicker can be a major workplace problem for anybody.

Another benefit is longer lamp and ballast life. This translates into large savings over time. Also, it takes fewer electronic ballasts to drive the same number of lamps, and even though electronic ballasts have a larger initial cost, the energy savings and the ballast-to-lamp ratio can pay back the difference in short order.

So what's the catch? Harmonics. But before we get to that story, it should be pointed out that if lamps are not properly matched with the appropriate ballasts, much of the efficiency benefit will be lost. Operating a mismatched lamp/ballast combination can result in higher power consumption, lower light output, and (you guessed it) excessive current harmonics.

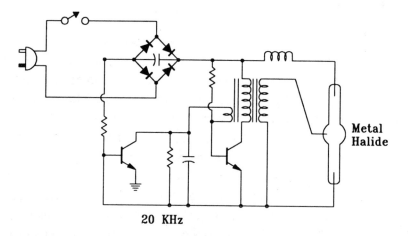

Figure 4-2. *A circuit for an electronic ballast. Notice the input diode bridge.*

What this means to the building manager or facilities engineer is clear. Even armed with all of the information from the rest of this chapter and utilizing a proper design, harmonics can still be a hazard if maintenance personnel do not use the right replacement lamps. Bargain replacements may create the old "pay me now or pay me later" scenario.

Electronic Ballast Harmonics

It would be nice at this point to display a typical electronic ballast signature and to draw some very wise conclusions about it. One such picture is shown in *Figure 4-3*. The problem is that there is a wide variation in the current distortion created by various models from various manufacturers. Unlike the situation with switching power supplies in PCs, the electronic ballast problem is a moving target. In addition, there is a perception that the THD is the important specification to look for. An often heard tome is that electronic ballasts have no greater THD than the older magnetic ballasts. This may seem reasonable as long as the harmonic analysis bears this out on a harmonic by harmonic basis, but it does no good to replace a magnetic ballast that has 50% THD with an electronic one that only has

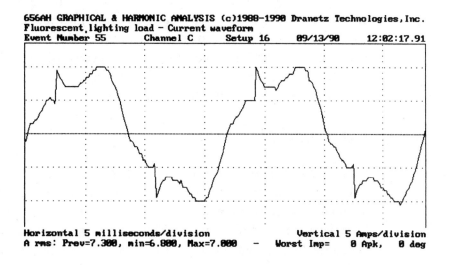

Figure 4- 3. *Current drawn by a high-efficiency electronic ballast. There is a wide variation in the distortion from different ballast designs.*
(Courtesy of Dranetz Technologies)

20% THD, if the zero sequenced harmonic content is greater. By the same token, it does no good to replace one ballast with another of lower THD if the second ballast draws more harmonic current. It is the magnitude of harmonic current, not the percentage, that has a practical impact on building electrical circuits. Lowering the THD does not guarantee that the building won't burn down or that the transformer won't fail. But before we look at the third harmonic, let's look at harmonics in general.

The technology of lighting has changed rapidly in recent years. Unfortunately, not every facility has changed with the technology. This means that for older facilities, the situation may be critical. And, at construction time, the National Electrical Code may not have mandated safe wiring practices that are found in the code today.

Older electronic lamp/ballast combinations can be expected to have current THDs up to nearly 60%, and they may well be configurations that are no longer recommended by manufacturers. In this same framework, the THD levels of older magnetic ballast configurations can be expected to range from about 15 - 35%. So-called energy savers can range to over 45%. For newer electronic ballast configurations, many have THDs that exceed 30%. Most manufacturers these days offer too low THD ballasts in addition to their standard product. Usually these are rated at 20% THD and 10% THD with commensurate pricing at each level. It should be noted that much of this information is consistent from 120v systems to 277v systems. The performance characteristics vary widely by manufacturer, lamp/ballast configuration, and voltage level. Since THD has become the "darling" specification of consulting engineers, it is one of those out-front specs and model delineators that manufacturers have detailed information about.

The Dreaded Third Harmonic

By far the largest single harmonic to define current draw for electronic ballasts is the dreaded third. *Table 4-1* shows a number of ballasts and the distribution of harmonics. Notice that the first five magnetic ballasts generally have significantly lower levels of the third harmonic. This phenomenon is not limited to fluorescent lighting ballasts. Similar findings are common for other lighting technologies, such as those using high pressure sodium.

We see from *Table 4-1* that it is possible in some ballast/lamp configurations to approach the same levels of third harmonic that are produced by switching power supplies. On the 277v side of things, these problems can be manageable

Ballast	Volts	Irms(mA)	I1(mA)	I3(%)	I5(%)	I7(%)	I9(%)
Standard 1	112.7	852	838	17.0	7.0	2.0	1.2
Standard 2	112.5	818	810	12.3	6.3	2.0	1.3
Energy Saving 1	112.4	774	762	16.0	8.0	.0	1.5
Energy Saving 2	112.5	621	612	16.0	5.7	2.3	1.7
Energy Saving 3	112.5	769	763	11.0	6.7	1.7	1.3
Electronic 1	112.5	640	610	30.7	4.6	4.3	2.5
Electronic 2	112.6	590	559	26.0	20.3	2.7	5.3
Electronic 3	112.4	591	579	17.0	8.3	5.0	1.7
Electronic 4	112.5	524	517	20.0	10.0	9.0	5.0
Electronic 5	112.5	802	545	79.3	53.3	33.3	25.0

Table 4-1. *The harmonic distortion of a variety of ballasts is shown here. Pay particular attention to the level of third harmonic.* (Courtesy of BMI)

from a facilities standpoint, but when 120v ballasts are intermixed on the same load center with single phase electronic office equipment, the problems associated with triplen harmonics can rapidly reach dangerous levels.

Ballast manufacturers are well aware of these issues and have addressed them in their designs. As we said earlier, it is typical to find "low harmonic" models on the order of 10% or 20% THD. However, one should look deeper than THD alone. Often in low THD versions, the fifth harmonic is sacrificed for the third. While lowering THD by a factor of 13%, it has been found that fifth harmonic current may increase by as much as 130%.

What this trade-off means is something we will explore further in a later chapter. Briefly, the trade-off between the third and fifth harmonic saves the neutral conductor at the expense of the transformer. As we will see later, transformer heating is a function of harmonic frequency rather than of THD. Since the fifth harmonic is 300 Hz, its heating effect is far greater than the third, which is 180 Hz. Lowering THD while increasing harmonic frequencies is like robbing Peter to pay Paul. We are simply moving the fire hazard from the neutral conductor to the transformer.

Ballast Conclusions

In some ways the electronic ballast issue makes the entire harmonic topic a bit confusing. As we have seen, ballasts display a wide variety of harmonic currents that vary by type, model, manufacturer, and lamp matching. Whereas in previous chapters we could point to PCs as culprits, here we find blame a little harder to place.

It forces us to think of something we should have been looking at all along—building design. Harmonic loads are not something we can shoot with a gun or cover with a bandage. They present phenomena that must be measured, planned for, and designed into the overall electrical structure of the facility. But before we take action, we need to be able to understand some of the less obvious power quality problems associated with single phase harmonics. To do this, we need to understand how to measure both harmonic currents and their effects.

5 Power Quality Problems:
Harmonics and the Ground Path

As a power quality practitioner, I run into some of the strangest problems. Lately, harmonics have been playing an ever increasing role. In this chapter, I want to relate some of the site specific problems that I have confronted only to find single phase harmonics and its effects staring back at me.

One of the principles that power quality practitioners must understand in order to solve any problem is that the responses of electrical circuits vary with frequency. Every site, piece of equipment, or circuit has a wide variety of factors that contribute to stray paths, mutual coupling, and distributed capacitance, and there's one thing that ties all of these elements together in an odd, metallic electrical path—ground.

It seems strange that harmonics and grounding would come together at all, but they do, often in ways that don't make sense unless we understand the relationship between circuits, frequency, and unwanted current flow.

At 60 Hz, everything seems wonderful. Electricity flows up one conductor and down another. Current is rectified, equipment functions, and life is good. But as soon as we inject large amounts of current at a frequency that the system was not designed to conduct, bizarre effects begin to manifest themselves.

The neat and tidy 60 Hz world looks completely different at 180 Hz or 10 MHz. A straight wire can act like an inductor. Two wires close together can be a short circuit. Energy can more easily be coupled from one part of the system to another, through inductive or capacitive elements that are not even discreet electrical or electronic components. This coupling is nearly always from the active current carrying parts of the system to the passive parts that are not supposed to carry working or signal current at all. These passive parts all have one thing in common: they are all part of the metal member of the building's grounding system. With that introduction, let's look at four situations where harmonics got tangled up with ground, and see what odd symptoms manifested themselves.

The Case of the Hum Bar Holiday

These strange problems always seem to occur over Thanksgiving or Christmas, and this case was no exception. I got a desperate call one afternoon from a former client, a Hollywood post production house.

Frankly, I was surprised to hear from them. They were difficult people to deal with. They argued with me and followed a course of action quite different from my recommendations. As I learned, video and audio engineers believe that Ohm's law does not apply to grounding. This erroneous hypothesis led them to ask me to return.

After my previous trip, they had managed to mask over their basic grounding problem by laying bus bars under the studio floor to form an "isolated" ground. Of course, all this did was form a ground loop between the bus bar system and the safety grounding system. Sometimes a misguided approach will solve an immediate problem, but a land mine is laid that may or may not be set off by the installation, movement, or upgrade of sensitive equipment.

This was a case of all three. When I arrived, I discovered that the building had a new addition. The studio had doubled in size. The problem was that any time they connected anything from the old part of the studio to the new studio, "hum bars" appeared in the video. The only way they could continue to function was to disconnect the signal cable and the "isolated ground" bar that ran from the old part of the building to the new part.

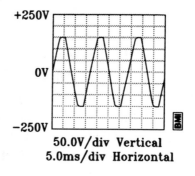

50.0V/div Vertical
5.0ms/div Horizontal

Figure 5-1. *Video studio line to neutral wave.*
The voltage waveform is flat topped.

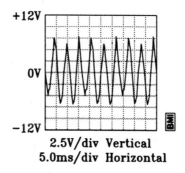

2.5V/div Vertical
5.0ms/div Horizontal

Figure 5-2. *Video studio neutral to ground voltage had a frequency three times that of the line voltage. Also notice that the waveform contains a 60 Hz component.*

Electric current, if you give it twenty paths to follow, will divide up according to Ohm's law, and some current will flow in all twenty paths. But there was something funny about this current! *Figure 5-1* shows the line voltage. Notice how the voltage sine wave is flat topped. This is the first sign of the true problem, switching power supplies. The flat topping is caused by all of that current, and the voltage drop is caused by its pulse wave shape.

Next came the neutral to ground voltage waveform. Notice that the trace on the BMI 2400 shows three times as many full wave cycles as the line to neutral waveform did (*Figure 5-2*). Using a Fluke meter capable of reading frequency, I confirmed my suspicions by pushing the "Hz" button. It read 180 Hz—the third harmonic!

A couple of questions come to mind. First of all, why do we see 180 Hz voltage from neutral to ground? Second, why does this waveform look like current and not voltage? After all, since the neutral and ground are bonded at the transformer, shouldn't we see 0?

The answers to these questions lie in a simple and famous mathematical law called Ohm's law (E = I x Z). If we are measuring voltage from neutral to ground, that simply means current must be flowing in one conductor with respect to the other. In this case, the studio was full of racks and racks of switching power supplies. All of these devices create a large third harmonic flowing in the common neutral. That pulsed phase current must flow back down the neutral conductor all the way to the source transformer. This flow "I" across the conductor "Z" creates a voltage drop "E" with respect to ground. Since this is 180 Hz, the impedance of the neutral conductor at that frequency is three times what it is at 60 Hz ($X_L = 2\pi$ f L). Therefore, the voltage drop is three times larger than would have been created by the same RMS current created by a linear load. But reality can be worse than theory. The neutral to ground voltage is only a symptom. Further measurements revealed 6 amps of current flowing in the ground path from the old building to the new addition, and this current was 180 Hz.

How can this be? Doesn't load current flow back to its source? Obviously, in this case, current is flowing back to its source through one or more ground loop paths that include the shield on the signal cables, and that is how the "hum" is being injected into the system. But a more fundamental question is, how is 180 Hz neutral current getting on ground in the first place? Traditionally, this would be caused by a wiring error—a neutral to ground reversal or short somewhere downstream of the transformer. Since this was not the case at the studio, I had to look elsewhere.

There were really only two possibilities, and both involved capacitance. The first place to start would be the noise filter inside each separate device's power supply. This filter contains a capacitor or capacitors connected from the power supply input to ground. This filter is for noise suppression, and is used in order to meet FCC requirements. The capacitor (or capacitors) has significant leakage at 180 Hz and bypasses some neutral current directly to ground. In addition, there is distributed capacitance. This is caused by running the neutral conductor through conduit, something we do every day. The mere fact that the neutral is in close proximity to ground means that stray capacitance forms along the run. Naturally, this is more critical as frequency goes higher and more neutral current can be bypassed to ground. There may be other stray paths from neutral to ground anywhere capacitance is found in the system.

So what do I do for these folks? I have two options: one is to eliminate the ground loops; the other is to eliminate or dramatically reduce the neutral current. In this case, there was no way the client would opt for good grounding practices. The only alternative was to get as much current off of the common neutrals as possible.

We accomplished this with the application of isolation transformers with center-tapped secondaries. We will talk more about this approach in the next chapter. For now, the point is that a transformer with no neutral on its input will stop the neutral current at that point. If this is far enough downstream, it may reduce system neutral current enough to get rid of associated problems. That is what happened in this case.

The Case of the Ground Current Contraption

I call it a contraption because that's exactly what it looked like sitting there in the newly remodeled office area. It was a PDU (power distribution unit), which is a Delta/Wye transformer in a portable cabinet. Usually you see these populating computer rooms, sitting on raised floors, providing power to large computer systems and peripherals.

In this case, management had wanted a "clean" electrical environment, so a PDU had been installed to be a power source for premises wiring due to its isolation transformer. Had it not been for the PDU, they might never have known they had a problem. It turned out that the PDU was giving periodic ground current alarms that exceeded the 5 amp alarm threshold.

Figure 5-3 shows the output phase currents and voltage from the PDU. *Figure 5-4* shows the neutral current and the ground current. These measurements were taken inside the PDU at the main output conductors. Notice again that the ground current is about 5 amps peak and is obviously 180 Hz.

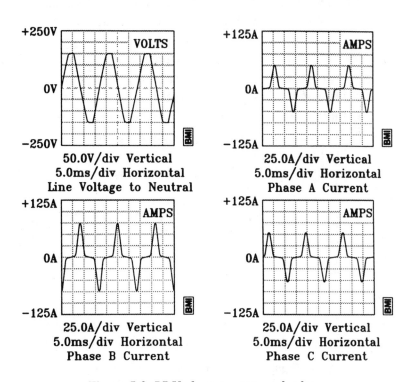

Figure 5-3. *PDU phase currents and voltage.*

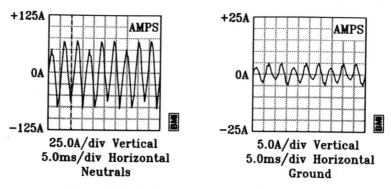

Figure 5-4. *PDU neutral current and ground current. Notice that the ground current is also 180 Hz.*

Next, look at *Figure 5-5*. Quite by accident, I caught a load coming on line when I was looking at a branch circuit, green wire, ground going to a telecommunications closet. This was proof that neutral current was getting on the ground conductors.

The input of the PDU had three different grounds; the conduit ground, a green wire ground, and a cold water ground. Notice that there is nothing on the cold water ground. The conduit safety ground shows a tiny bit of 180 Hz current being modulated by a bit of 60 Hz, and the green wire shows very little. This told me that nearly all of the offending neutral current was emanating from and returning to the PDU (*Figure 5-6*).

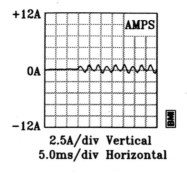

Figure 5-5. *When an electronic device cycles on in the telecom room, look what happens to branch circuit ground current.*

So what do we have? Again, this is a case of distributed, stray, and leakage capacitance, and in this case is probably no cause for concern. While undesirable, a few amps on ground is probably typical in areas like this for the reasons discussed. It probably will not cause operational or safety problems, but to eliminate it would mean getting rid of the large 180 Hz neutral current. In many ways, the real problem was the PDU. Without the PDU there would be no alarm. Interestingly enough, the use of a PDU to feed premises wiring is both a violation of the NEC and the UL listing of the PDU.

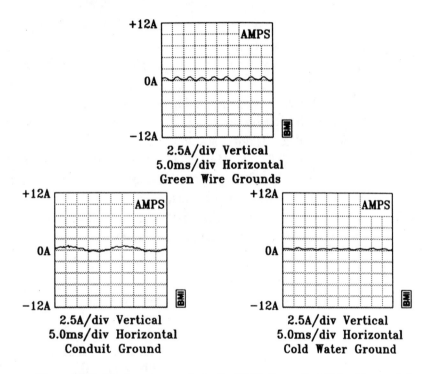

Figure 5-6. *The input grounds to the PDU shows that little, if any, of the ground current was being circulated upstream of the PDU.*

The Case of the Secret Screens

Every now and then, I get into one of those secured areas inside a government contracting facility where secret research is going on. In this case, it was a newly remodeled area. I was escorted everywhere I went. People were instructed to blank their screens, and my escort carried a lunchbox-looking device that honked every few seconds and had a flashing red light. I felt special.

The problem was that nearly everyone used large screens in their workstations. In certain areas of the building, the screens shimmied so badly that it drove the operators crazy. *Figure 5-7* shows the neutral current on one of many panels in the area.

Further investigation revealed the following facts. The feeders to the panels ran under the area of the building experiencing the problem. These were plastic conduit buried in concrete. There was a likelihood that these conduits also contained an abandoned feeder that ran from one building to another. All of the loads consisted of computers and 120v electronic ballasts.

You may have already guessed what was happening. Leakage magnetic fields from the feeders were interfering with the electron beams inside the CRTs. In fact, a measurement of the fields using a magnetic lug and a scope revealed that the waveform of the field looked like neutral current.

I had always been taught that the magnetic fields cancel in a feeder. That is correct with two exceptions. First, if the geometry of the feeder conductors is not uniform and consistent in spacing, you will always have some residual ballooning out further than is desireable. In addition, the near field is proportional to the peak of the current and with high neutral currents in excess of phase currents, the effect of the field will be stronger. Plastic conduit doesn't help much, either. Ferrous metallic conduit tends to close the field, preventing much of the field energy from extending too far beyond the metal cylinder.

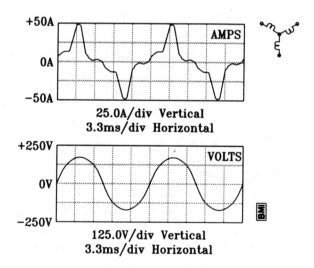

Figure 5-7. *Panel neutral current.*

The other exception is more complex. For the magnetic field to cancel evenly and completely, all of the current must be flowing in the conduit and its contained wires, or in its wires only. Where would it be possible for current to escape the planned circuit path? Ground paths, of course. If significant current is flowing in the ground path and there are ground loops, then the total current will not flow in the conduit's circuit. This imbalance results in an uncancelled magnetic field.

This was a complex situation and very hard to sort out, especially since the feeders were inaccessible. But my theory was that since significant 180 Hz neutral current was flowing, a combination of near field strength, geometry, capacitive leakage of neutral current to ground, and unbalanced current flow conspired to create interfering magnetic fields and a fine mess in a brand new area.

The problem was the fix. Magnetic shielding is a strange and expensive proposition. Each offended CRT would need a special metal box put around it at a cost of about $1,200. Other alternatives were to reroute feeders overhead in metal conduit, or to eliminate the harmonic problems, or both, and nothing carried an absolute guarantee.

The Case of the Harmonic that Hertz

I was called out to inspect a PDU that was giving another ground current alarm. This story has a strange twist that makes revisiting the ground current issue worthwhile.

This facility was so secret that only the national press and TV cameras were allowed to see what was going on. They blindfolded me after several security stops and removed the blindfold so I could tell them where the ground current was coming from as I stood in front of a PDU inside an electrical room. After several hours of tracing circuits and taking measurements, I felt as though the blindfold was still firmly in place even after it was removed.

The PDU fed a room full of top-secret, extremely high-powered workstations. Interestingly enough, the workstations were powered by both 60 Hz and 400 Hz, and they were enclosed within a Tempest room, where the walls were shielded and RF filters were connected to all of the feeders entering the room to ground.

There was a mixture of "house" power, "clean" power, and 400 Hz power. Between the various power sources, the shield, and all of the grounding schemes, it took me a long time to sort out all of the potential ground loops to get to the real issues. Also, I was informed that the room had been experiencing another problem in addition to the ground current alarm on the PDU: the 400 Hz RF filters had been burning up.

I'd like to show you a picture of what I found, but I was not allowed to leave with any printouts. But it was the same old stuff—180 Hz neutral current running throughout all of the ground loops. What was nice about this particular situation was that the neutral current from the switching power supplies not only explained the ground current alarm, it also explained the failing filters.

A filter designed to have a particular reactance at radio frequencies acts to block the propagation of those frequencies for which it was designed, but at 180 Hz it may be a short circuit or have some parasitic resonance with some stray capacitance nearby. What was happening in this case was that the neutral current on ground was somehow seeing the RF filters as a low impedance path. Enough 180 Hz current was passed by the filters that current ratings were being exceeded and a failure of components resulted. This was just a theory, but the presence of unplanned for power frequencies always has unpredictable consequences.

PQ Wrap Up

These are typical of the single phase harmonic issues I have seen as power quality problems. I have read references to radio frequency radiation caused by harmonics, but I have not encountered it. But this issue of grounding has been prevalent in my consulting practice. One area in which I have not seen it (but I know I will) is local area networks. The potential differences and current flows at 180 Hz are problems for any equipment networked to other devices.

My basic purpose in including this chapter was to share my experiences and to stimulate thinking as to the implications of 180 Hz currents being injected into the electrical environment to the magnitude shown here. You may want to go back and look at the peak neutral currents and view this in terms of coupling. There is certainly enough current that even a little pumped into the grounding system will create a variety of bizarre power quality problems. It's time to move on to understand how to solve these problems and how to make buildings safer and more "friendly."

6 Single Phase Harmonics: Solutions

Before we get to all of the solutions that can be applied to the single phase harmonics problem, let's summarize the problem itself. We have the issue of overheated neutrals due to the non-cancellation of triplen harmonics. We touched briefly on the skin effect and the problems associated with heating due to higher order harmonic frequencies. The skin effect basically decreases the effective cross sectional area available for the flow of current, thereby increasing resistance.

There are three problems we need to address related to single phase harmonics. The first is the safety issue of the neutrals. Here we have a conductor that will likely be overloaded, carrying current in excess of its rated ampacity at the point where the single-phase neutrals are brought together in a three phase system.

The second problem is related to overheating caused by the skin effect and other high frequency current effects, like eddy currents, and hysteresis in transformers, and I^2R drops. This leads to transformer failures, red hot bus bars, and nuisance tripping of breakers, just to name a few.

The final problem associated with single phase harmonics is power quality. In the last chapter we explored how neutral current interacted with the grounding system. Harmonic currents can be associated with interfering noise due to connections that loosen because of thermal stress. Also, harmonic currents nearly always result in some sort of voltage distortion. This distortion can be the source of motors overheating and of decreased ride-through in power supplies. It is important to keep these three things in mind when attacking the single phase harmonics problem. One approach will not always solve other problems.

There are two basic strategies that can be used to deal with the single phase harmonics problem. First, we can cope with harmonic currents by a design or redesign approach that safely deals with the excess heating and currents. Second, we can apply product technologies to eliminate or divert the harmonics. In this chapter, we will look at both.

Coping

Coping is a somewhat negative word, but what we mean to imply here is to adapt to an anticipated or pre-existing condition. Coping involves either designing for harmonic loads and the conditions that may occur or by adopting a strategy for dealing with what is already taking place in an existing facility.

The basic question to ask is, how will the electrical infrastructure deal with the presence of harmonic currents? Obviously this assumes that we will not be able to go out and buy a black box to put on every load to stop the problem. Our design or present system must adequately cope with the problem. This is much easier if we are dealing with a new building or the retrofit of an existing facility. This gives us a chance to take care of harmonics issues in the design phase. The major problem here is anticipating the worst case scenario. Every designer knows that five minutes after tenants move into a space, all of the loads have a habit of changing and growing. One engineer told me that his "rule of thumb" was to give the client all the capacity he could and to keep his fingers crossed. It is not unusual to see special purpose buildings or computer rooms designed for 35 watts per square foot being driven to nearly twice that usage. The implication for harmonics and the safety issues surrounding them is a serious one for the designer.

For the facilities manager in an existing facility, the issues are different and more complex. He may or may not be able to change building wiring, and may or may not be able to purchase mitigating equipment. In the end, this situation must involve top management and facilities management, as well as users. The resulting strategy will include the application of planned load growth, regular measurements and analysis, and some application of both infrastructure upgrades and product applications.

One final and absolutely critical point needs to be made. There can be rules of thumb applied, but the entire facility is now a computer room. By that I mean that electronic loads in heavy concentration are peppered throughout nearly every facility. Harmonics and their impact need to be evaluated on a department by department basis. Each distinct work area has its own unique characteristics and must be evaluated in and of itself.

The Neutral

More has been written about the neutral than any other harmonics topic in recent years. Basically our mission is clear. We must figure out a way to handle the uncancelled harmonic current in the neutral. Remember that this current is likely to be on the order of 1.73 times greater than on the most heavily loaded phase.

As we saw in Chapter 3, the ampacity of a #10 conductor is 35 amps, and the ampacity of a #12 conductor is 25 amps. If a 20 amp circuit breaker is used, the NEC allows the connected load for continuous operation to be 80% of the circuit breaker rating, or 16 amps. If we assume that the circuit is fully loaded and the neutral is carrying 150% in a 3 phase 4 wire system, then the neutral current will be 24 amps. If we assume 200%, the current would be 32 amps. Note that the NEC does not define amp by frequency. An amp is an amp, at 60 Hz or 100 Hz.

One of the most common recommended practices to alleviate the neutral current problem is to upsize the neutral to the next larger size (*Figure 6-1*), so a #12 becomes a #10, and a #10 becomes a #8. A rule of thumb for standard office circuits is to use #10s. In many cases this may be sufficient. However, in cases where neutral current is excessive, going up two sizes may be proper.

In order to understand which neutral to use, a careful evaluation of loads is necessary. You can see that this is not simple and straightforward. In general, the ampacity of a shared neutral must be twice that of the phase conductors. This applies not only to branch circuit neutrals but to load center feeders as well.

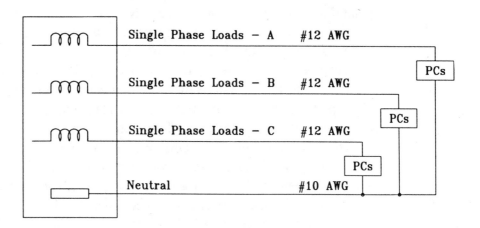

Figure 6-1. *Common neutral must be upsized to carry significant additive third harmonic current from phases A,B,C.*

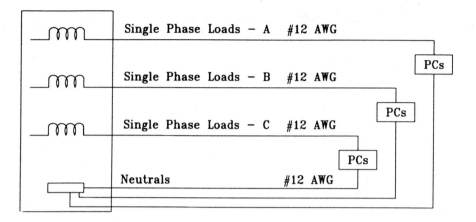

Figure 6-2. *Separate neutrals prevent phase current harmonics from adding in the neutral.*

Separate Neutrals

For branch circuit neutrals, another answer would be to run separate neutral conductors. This would mean that for each phase conductor in the standard 42 pole panel board, we would have forty-two neutral conductors. (This would direct the return current for each phase branch circuit back down its own discreet neutral. Triplen harmonics cannot add from the three phases until they reach a point where they are brought together. The first common point would be the load center neutral bus bar.) The strategy behind this is that neutrals will never carry current greater than their associated phase conductors.

This does not mean that branch circuit receptacles cannot be daisy chained in the normal fashion. The same standards of practice would be applied as before. The separate neutral design simply means that for each breaker, there is a corresponding phase conductor and a white neutral conductor (*Figure 6-2*).

This is not as simple as it seems. We need to have load centers with neutral bus bars capable of handling forty-two white wires, plus we may well have conduit, panel board, and wireway and other raceway fill problems due to so many wires. Obviously, the easiest place to accommodate this is in the design phase of new construction or remodeling. However, this is a relatively expensive solution and it doesn't just stop with the neutral conductor. The load centers themselves may need to be rated for harmonics. Also, specially rated breakers may need to be specified. The feeders neutral will typically need a 2X rating, as will the panel's neutral bus. This is important if we don't want to simply "fix" the branch circuit problems and move them to the panel and feeder. By running separate neutrals, we may have removed the safety hazard from the work area, but other hazards lurk in the electrical room, the biggest of which is the transformer.

Derating Transformers

There are two approaches in handling harmonics and power source transformers, either single phase or three phase. The first calls for derating the transformer for harmonic loads. However, it should be noted that the NEC and Underwriter's Laboratory do not recognize derating. The other method is to use a specially designed transformer called a K-factor or K-rated transformer. We will discuss those in Chapter 10.

The typical building transformer is a Delta/Wye transformer. Single phase lighting and appliance loads are accommodated either with a 480/Y277 secondary or a 208/Y120 secondary, but the real transformer story starts in the primary winding.

A transformer uses current to create a magnetic field (flux). Unfortunately, flux is not linearly proportional to its magnetizing current. The waveform in *Figure 6-3* has a significant component of third harmonic. To prevent this from distorting the upstream bus voltage, a Delta winding is used to insure a relatively sinusoidal voltage. Thus, the Delta windings become a recirculating path for triplen harmonics that produces little associated flux.

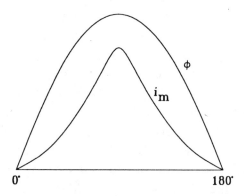

Figure 6-3. *This simplified diagram shows that the magnetizing current of a transformer is non-linear compared to flux (ϕ). The current contains triplen harmonics.*

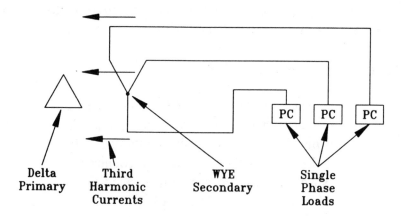

Delta   Third   WYE   Single
Primary   Harmonic   Secondary   Phase
           Currents   Loads

Figure 6-4. *The balanced third harmonic current is in phase in the Delta primary and cannot flow upstream.*

If we connect loads that produce triplen harmonic current across all three phases, these currents will produce an associated magnetomotive force in the primary. For most harmonic current, what you see on the output is reflected on the input of the transformer. The Delta winding, however, provides paths for the triplen magnetomotive forces that are in phase and produce little triplen harmonic current at the primary. In effect, the third and odd multiples of the third are trapped in the primary line circuit conductors upstream (*Figure 6-4*). There is one caveat to this. The phases must be balanced, or else the unbalanced geometric sum of the triplens will be reflected upstream.

Delta/Wye transformers sound like the answer to triplen harmonics, but not exactly. They can be part of a solution, but the point here is that substantial harmonic current can be circulating in the primary of a transformer and might not be measured on the primary side. A transformer that appears to be 75% loaded might possibly be 150% loaded! When we add to this the fact that the transformer was never designed to dissipate the heat caused by the losses associated with harmonics, we have a potential for transformer failures.

To take this into account, one of the earliest methods was developed by the Computer Business Equipment Manufacturers Association (CBEMA), who recommended that distribution transformers be derated according to the crest factor of the load. The derating equation is: Derating Factor = (1.414) x average RMS phase current/peak phase current.

This formula takes the distorted RMS current and compares it to a pure sine wave by multiplying it by the crest factor for a sine wave. The result is then divided by the actual instantaneous peak of the distorted current. The result is a number between 0 and 1. We use the average RMS current to account for possible imbalances in the phase loading.

Let's say that the average phase current was 100 amps RMS and that the peak currents were 300 amps. This would give us a ratio of 141.4 amps to 300, or a derating factor of .5. Using this method we would conclude that this transformer should not be loaded more than 50%. In the real world, these derating factors usually work out to be between .5 - .7.

Caution! This method of derating is not recognized by the NEC or Underwriter's Laboratory. It should only be considered a rule of thumb, and it will not absolve you of liability. The transformer manufacturer will no doubt not stand behind the product if it was designed for linear loads and fails under non-linear conditions regardless of derating. This also could be considered an NEC and listing violation. This is the subject of some controversy by uninformed persons, but checking with the manufacturer, as well as with UL and the electrical inspector for the site, is a good idea.

Transformer Solutions

We have already talked about how Delta/Wye transformers trap triplen harmonics. It seems obvious that one potential solution to the single phase harmonic problem would be to replace one large Delta/Wye transformer with several of

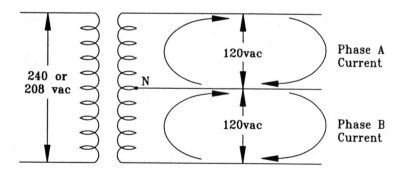

Figure 6-5. *In this single phase isolation transformer there is no neutral, and secondary phase currents are 180° out of phase in the neutral.*

them placed close to the offending loads. The effect of this would be to break up the high neutral currents and keep them at manageable levels.

Another solution using transformers is the application of a split phase or dual phase transformer (*Figure 6-5*). This was what we did in the video studio in Chapter 5. This transformer uses two phase conductors on its primary and establishes the neutral on the secondary. The benefit is that current in the neutral from phase A is 180° out of phase with current from phase B, thereby cancelling the neutral current. However, the extent of cancellation does depend on load balancing and the amount of synchronization of the load current waveforms.

In the case of the audio studio, this worked great since the ground noise was coming from the neutral. However, we must recognize that while this cures the hot neutral problem, it does nothing for the phase conductors and any excess heating or nuisance tripping of breakers. Harmonic currents still circulate throughout the phase conductors, transformer, and any load center located upstream. However, applying this as a fix is much easier in many cases than rewiring or pulling larger conductors.

The "Zigzag" Solution

Here's a device worth looking at, and frankly, I'm not sure a lot of folks are aware this even exists. It's called a zigzag autotransformer (*Figure 6-6* shows how a zigzag works). The transformer in the diagram is represented as vectors. Notice how the transformer removes current from the neutral and places it onto the phase conductors. This is the beauty of the zigzag approach.

It is connected to the 3 phase 4 wire system. It has six identical windings that are arranged in the vectorial relationship you see in the figure. Imagine that the load is drawing three amps. Notice that neutral current is shunted through the zigzag and returns in the other two phases. If the transformer were perfect, total elimination of the third harmonic would result. The zigzag not only dramatically reduces triplen harmonics, but it takes all neutral current and transfers it into the phases. As a result, maximum peak currents in each phase are reduced by 1/3, and upstream neutral currents are virtually eliminated, even if the phases are unbalanced. This elimination of upstream neutral current is effective not only for the third harmonic but for all neutral harmonic currents, as well as any unbalanced component of fundamental current.

Zigzag transformers are small, relatively light, and easy to add in the power distribution systems, but we cannot attempt this approach with ordinary trans-

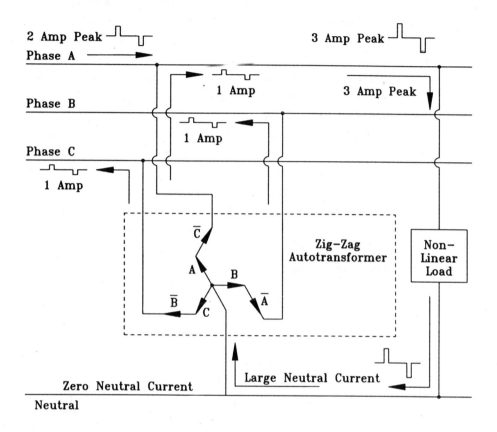

Figure 6-6. *Vector diagram of zigzag to transformer.*

former technology. Just as with standard building transformers, zigzags are subject to the same heating caused by eddy currents and skin effect due to harmonic current flow. Manufacturers of these devices have taken this into consideration and prefer to call their products "Zero Sequenced Harmonic Filters." It should be noted that these devices must have both overcurrent protection on the connections to each phase and some kind of neutral current alarm on the filter neutral bus.

Filters

There are a number of other devices on the market in the form of filters, both active and passive, that attempt to solve the single phase harmonic problem. A passive filter uses some values of capacitance and inductance to change the current waveform. An active filter uses power semiconductors to interact with load current such that its current wave shape contains less third harmonic content.

The main problem with both approaches is efficiency. 180 Hz is so close to 60 Hz that leakage current, as well as inductor saturation, becomes a significant problem. Obviously, any leakage will reduce efficiency. On the other hand, active filter elements are inherently somewhat inefficient by virtue of power conversion.

Of course, the other issue is cost. Typically, these filters are designed to plug in ahead of each offending single phase device. This means that in order to eliminate third harmonic current, a filter would have to be placed on each PC or other device with a single phase diode capacitor input.

This does not mean that these devices aren't effective and shouldn't be investigated. Three phase versions that are installed at transformers or panels can significantly reduce third harmonic current and may make economic sense for special applications.

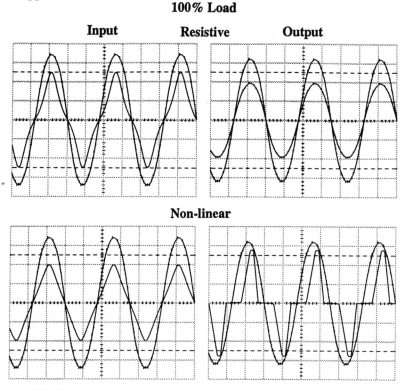

Figure 6-7. *This shows the input current waveforms of a ferroresonant based UPS. Notice that the wave shape is nearly independent of load current distortion even at 100% load.*

The Ferro Fix

Ferroresonant transformers (sometimes called CVTs or constant voltage transformers) are another solution to the single phase harmonics problem. The input current waveform for a ferro is not strictly load dependent (*Figure 6-7*). It is much more linear than that of a switch-mode power supply, and it is not rich in third harmonics. In addition, testing has shown that neutral current can be reduced up to 70% using ferros on switching power supplies.

Ferros also have the unique characteristic of being voltage regulators, and they can be found in some single phase UPS (uninterruptible power system) designs. A ferroresonant UPS is an excellent power conditioner or voltage regulator, and solves (to a large degree) the third harmonic problem. As with filters, solving single phase harmonics with ferros requires that one be placed on each PC or group of PCs.

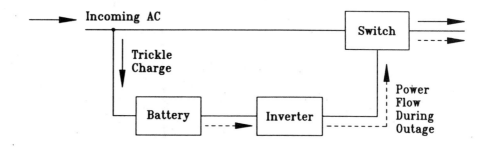

Figure 6-8. *SPS block diagram.*

UPSs—A Solution?

There are basically two types of UPSs (uninterruptible power systems). One is actually an SPS (standby power system); the other is an on-line design where incoming power is continuously converted from AC to DC and back to AC again. These are also referred to as double conversion UPSs. Whether or not a design is on line is an endless debate that we won't get into right now, but for our purposes, the difference is that in an SPS, no power conversion is taking place (*Figure 6-8*). The unit is basically passive or line interactive when called on until utility power goes out. In a double conversion UPS, the rectifier charger is continuously rectifying AC into DC (*Figure 6-9*).

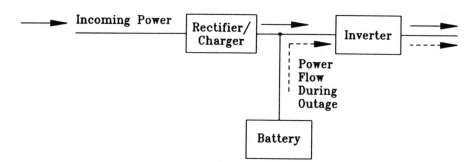

Figure 6-9. *UPS block diagram.*

Technology	Input Current THD
SPS	118.0%
SPS	119.0%
SPS	109.1%
SPS	103.0%
SPS	97.3%
SPS	115.0%
SPS	105.0%
SPS	89.0%
SPS	103.0%
SPS	105.7%
Ferro	13.7%
Ferro	11.6%
Ferro	12.6%
Ferro	13.3%
Line-Interactive	20.2%
Double-Conversion	158.3%
Double-Conversion	47.7%
Double-Conversion	16.4%
Double-Conversion	129.0%
Double-Conversion	120.0%
Double-Conversion	25.9%
Double-Conversion	68.4%
Double-Conversion	126.0%
Double-Conversion	106.0%
Double-Conversion	32.0%
Double-Conversion	23.3%

Table 6-1. *Input THD for most of the popular small SPS and UPSs.*

Table 6-1 shows the input total harmonic distortion for the most popular brands of UPS or SPS for single phase loads. With the exception of the ferro-based products and a couple of the double conversion designs, most of these devices have THD as bad as the loads they support. *Figure 6-10* shows the input waveform of one of the units. Notice that the input of the UPS must be a diode capacitor, just like a switching power supply.

The actual problem with double conversion single phase UPSs is even worse. Since they rarely run over 80 - 85% efficiency, they create more harmonic distortion than the loads they support. The THD of the SPS models is nothing more than a reflection of the load connected to them, except when they are charging their batteries, at which time that will add to the distortion somewhat.

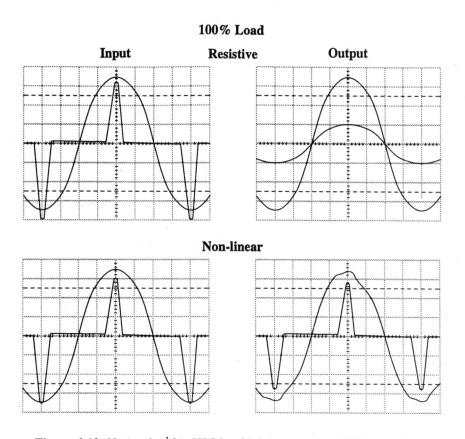

100% Load

Input   **Resistive**   **Output**

Non-linear

Figure 6-10. *Notice that this UPS has high input current THD even when the load is linear. It must have an input diode capacitor bridge.*

The Great PFC Debate

It may have occurred to you that it is about time the computer manufacturers faced up to the power supplies problem themselves. If the computer power supplies are the gremlins, couldn't they be fixed? The answer is yes. In Chapter 10, we will deal with the standards that have forced the move to what's called "PFCs" or power factor corrected power supplies.

Before we get into what this means, we need to understand a bit more about power factor. Traditionally, we think of displacement power factor or real power in watts divided by apparent power expressed by volts times amps, but only at the fundamental frequency of 60 Hz. In point of fact, there is a power factor for each harmonic as well, and to get total power factor we must take the total true power at all frequencies and divide by volt/amps.

To put it a different way, non-linear loads have two power factor components: displacement power factor and distortion power factor. Distortion power factor $= \sqrt{\frac{1}{(1+\text{THD})^2}}$. For our purposes here, it is not necessary to go into all of the equations that do this. What is important to understand is that distorted current of the type created by PCs results in poor power factor. So the term "power factor" is an-

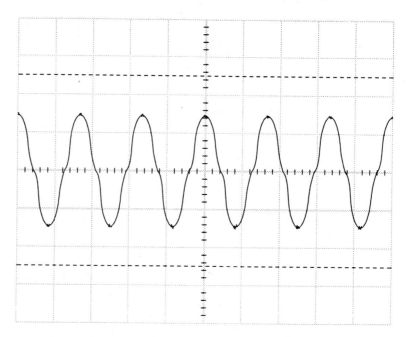

Figure 6-11. *The input PFC current wave shape when supplied by the utility. Notice that the pulses associated with a diode/capacitor input are not present.*

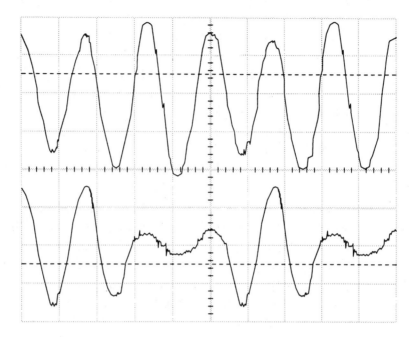

Figure 6-12. *This shows the interaction between a PFC and a ferro under laboratory conditions. The current oscillations (bottom) cause the voltage fluctuations (top).*

other way of expressing the results of harmonic distortion. To correct harmonic distortion, then, is to correct power factor.

When a designer comes up with a power supply that does not draw current in big pulses or gulps, but is more linear, he may call it a "power factor corrected" design, and that is what has happened. A whole new series of power supplies is coming to market which solves the third harmonic problem by using circuitry inside the power supply itself to correct the bad power factor of the diode/capacitor bridge. The shorthand term for them is "PFCs" (the current waveform of one PFC is shown in *Figure 6-11*).

We can expect to see PFCs in more and more electronic equipment, but we may not see them in all PCs (see Chapter 10). As with so many things in life, when we solve one problem we create another. It turns out that PFCs fall into this category. PFCs use either active or passive elements to correct the power factor, and these elements can interact with some source equipment to produce very undesirable results.

The worst problem that has been unearthed since the advent of PFCs is the interaction that occurs when a PFC is supplied by a ferroresonant transformer. *Figure 6-12* shows that a lightly loaded ferro will go into oscillation with a PFC load at only about 20% load. These current oscillations will cause corresponding voltage oscillations. If the ferro is part of a UPS, the UPS will determine that input voltage is not within tolerance, and the unit will go to battery. If the oscillation causes no further problem, the UPS will eventually drop the load when the battery is exhausted. If not, components will overheat, and the power supply will eventually shut down.

As you add other loads—even other PFC loads—to a ferro, the oscillation problem goes away. The PFC must be a specific type, with specific current elements to cause the interaction. As soon as you put other loads into the current waveform mix, the oscillation problem goes away. At this point, it appears the PFC issue is a real problem, but a problem that can only be simulated in the lab. The world's largest manufacturer of ferro-based UPSs, Best Power Technology, has fixed the problem anyway (*Figure 6-13*). It will be integrated into their future products and is a very simple add-on module for that rare site that might experience a problem.

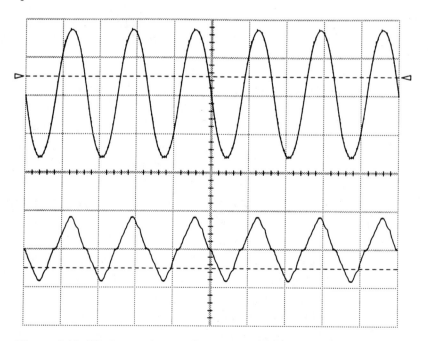

Figure 6-13. *The interactions no longer occur when the PFC is supplied by a ferro using a simple circuit on its output.*

Single Phase Conclusion

The first six chapters have covered an enormous amount of ground, both practical and theoretical, and this chapter has presented a potpourri of various strategies and solutions for single phase harmonics.

Some may be disappointed that I have not presented a "cookie cutter" approach or a standard recipe for fixing the problem. My professional philosophy has always been to use the most appropriate application of technology. Furthermore, it is the site itself that suggests the most appropriate course of action. The type of building, electrical infrastructure, economies, departmental patterns—all of these, and a host of other site-specific considerations, must be part of the equation. What works well in one area may not be appropriate in another.

For years, information technology and building technology have been on a collision course. Harmonics is a prime example of this problem, and it takes careful thought, analysis, planning, and installation to address the issue. It can't be done by contractors or facility managers in a vacuum. Solving the single phase harmonics problem must involve everyone in the organization.

There's one final point I'd like to make. Harmonics has been the source of building fires. I know of one fire in particular where harmonics may have been the cause; a maintenance man was killed in an elevator when he was sent to check out an alarm, and the elevator stopped at the fire. It is a life/safety issue that must be taken seriously and addressed immediately. I have heard that any manager or supervisor who knowingly ignores a potential safety hazard is criminally liable for injuries that might occur. In California there is a law to this effect, known as SB 6320. If for no other reason, management has a motive to fix the problem, even if to simply stay out of jail.

7 Notching: ASDs, VFDs, and UPSs

A static power converter is basically a rectifier that uses power semiconductors. The switching power supply is a static power converter that converts AC into DC. For the purposes of the remainder of this book, however, we will refer to static power converters, SPCs, as being three phase devices. UPSs are static power converters, and so are motor drives. Any electronic device that converts AC into DC for any purpose is an SPC.

The most widely used and fastest growing SPC is the ASD (adjustable speed drive), or VFD (variable frequency drive). Frankly, I am never sure what to call these SPCs. I do know what they do. They usually adjust the speed of a synchronous motor by varying the frequency. There are AC motor drives and DC motor drives, and the same forces that are pushing the installation of electronic lighting ballasts are behind the expansion of the VFD industry.

In the old days, motors were allowed to run at normal speed all the time. Process was then controlled by means of valves, vanes, or dampers. From an electrical standpoint, varying the process without varying the motor was inefficient. Using VFDs to control motor speed has such an impact on energy savings that paybacks in less than twelve months are not unusual.

The basic VFD consists of a rectifier used to convert AC to DC, a DC bus or link, and an inverter connected to the AC motor. UPSs use exactly the same building blocks except that batteries are connected to the DC bus to provide power during a utility outage, but for our purposes, we are really only concerned with the rectifier. There are any number of SPCs that use static power conversion for many reasons. It is the effect on the building's electrical distribution system with which we are primarily concerned. In order to understand this, we must take a few moments to look at the rectification process. Then we will be able to see how harmonic analysis fits into the picture.

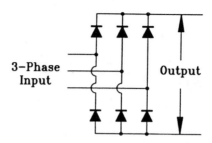

Figure 7-1. *A full-wave three phase bridge rectifier using diodes.*

Rectification

Figure 7-1 shows a three phase full-wave bridge rectifier. The result is the DC ripple current waveform shown in *Figure 7-2*. Diodes are used in many SPCs. The current harmonic content of this type of rectification is shown in *Figures 7-3a* and *7-3b*.

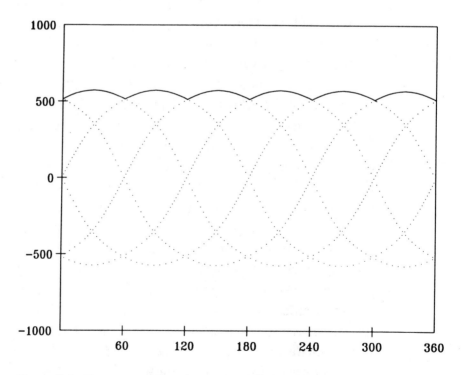

Figure 7-2. *The output ripple current of a three phase diode bridge is easier to filter than the output of a single phase bridge since the ripple frequency is higher.*

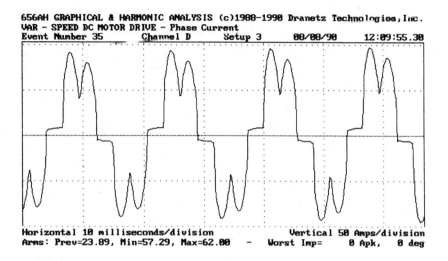

Figure 7-3a. *The current signature...*

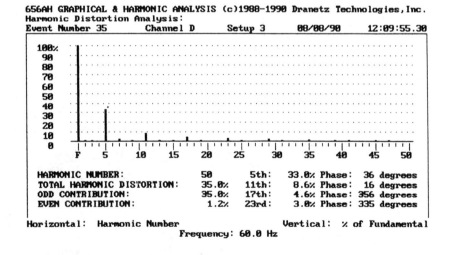

Figure 7-3b. *...and spectrum analysis of a three phase bridge rectifier.*
(Courtesy of Dranetz Technologies)

The other type of rectification we want to look at involves the use of SCRs, sometimes called thyristors. *Figure 7-4* shows how two SCRs might be used in a circuit. The SCR has a property a diode does not have. By applying a pulse to the gate, the SCR is turned on. Current will conduct until either the anode of the SCR is forced to zero, or until the current naturally falls to zero. Hence the terms "forced commutation" and "natural commutation." There is a device very similar to an SCR that can be turned off by applying a signal to the gate. This is called a gate turn off thyristor, or GTO.

Let's put SCRs in a full-wave bridge configuration and see what happens. This circuit (*Figure 7-5*) shows how using SCRs can control the magnitude of DC voltage to the inverter section. This is accomplished by controlling the conduction time (angle) of the SCRs. Logic circuits can control the voltage so that voltage from the inverter is adjusted while frequency is changed. This maintains a constant volts per hertz ratio to the motor.

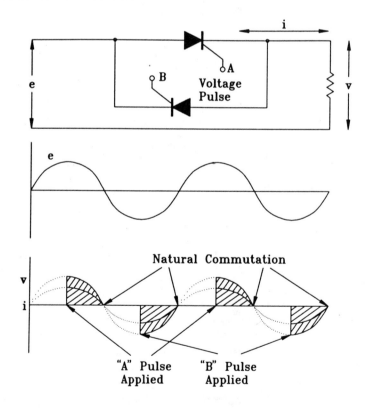

Figure 7-4. *Using two SCRs and applying pulses to the gates of the SCRs, we can use either forced or natural commutation to vary output current and voltage.*

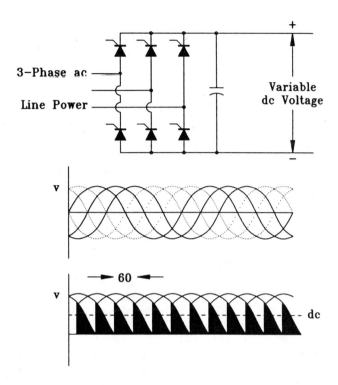

Figure 7-5. *In this full-wave thyristor bridge, DC voltage is varied by changing the conduction angle of the SCRs.*

Commutation and Notching

Whenever AC power is converted to DC power by a rectifier using a non-linear device, namely an SCR, the process of commutation occurs. We are going to step through this process to see what happens in terms of current and voltage distortion. *Figure 7-6* shows the same circuit as *Figure 7-5* with the addition of the various current signatures of each SCR. To simplify the analysis, let's assume that the bridge in Figure 7-6 consists of diodes rather than SCRs (an SCR fully phased on behaves like a diode).

Let's focus on D1 and 3. The conduction of each diode is dependent on the polarity and magnitude of the voltage presented across it. As the voltage across D1 peaks, the voltage across 3 starts to increase. At some point the voltages become equal as one goes down and the other goes up. Current flows through both diodes for the time it takes for the current to commutate from one diode to

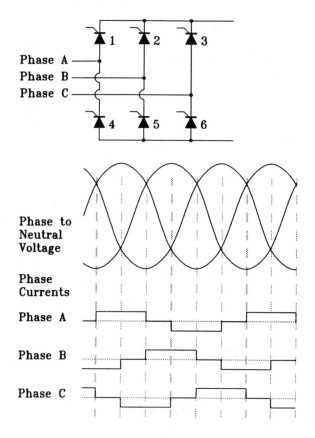

Figure 7-6. *The current and voltage relationships in a three phase bridge rectifier.*

the other. The process is similar when SCRs are used instead of diodes, except the ccmmutations occur at a delayed angle when the two voltages are not equal. For a brief moment, there is a phase-to-phase short between A and B. This short circuit causes the transformer secondary voltage to drop to a level determincd by the secondary impedance of the transformer and the magnitude of the short circuit current. The result is a notch in the voltage waveform. The number of notches is a function of the number of pulses or SCRs in the rectifier (*Figure 7-7*). Notch width becomes narrower since the total notch area is determined by circuit impedance. Notches are only present at the input of phase controlled rectifiers.

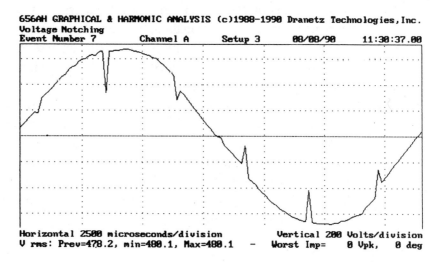

656AH GRAPHICAL & HARMONIC ANALYSIS (c)1988-1990 Dranetz Technologies,Inc.
Voltage Notching
Event Number 7   Channel A   Setup 3   08/08/90   11:30:37.00

Horizontal 2500 microseconds/division   Vertical 200 Volts/division
V rms: Prev=478.2, min=480.1, Max=480.1   -   Worst Imp=   0 Vpk,   0 deg

Figure 7-7. *This voltage waveform shows the notching that results from the current signature shown in Figure 7-6.* (Courtesy of Dranetz Technologies)

IEEE Std. 519-1992 has a fairly detailed explanation of all of this with the associated equations. Most of the power quality literature is replete with information on notching, but for the practitioner, most of it is just window dressing. The main thing we need to understand about harmonic distortion of voltage waveforms in the form of notches is that it is readily identifiable and causes a series of problems which make perfect sense. Let's look at some examples.

The Consultant's Case Book

I have been called out on a number of problems related to notching of the voltage sine wave. In each case, the problem manifested itself a little differently, but in all cases, the affected equipment was behaving strangely due to the notches.

In one case, I was called into a bank processing center. Every time a check sorter was turned on and began to cycle, the main CPU shut down. I observed that the voltage waveform had significant notching *(Figure 7-8)*. On further investigation, I discovered that the CPU had a special circuit in its power supply that detected power outages and shut down the CPU. It became clear that the notches were somehow biasing the transistor in the shut-off circuit. This happened despite the presence of an RC network with a time constant that was a lot longer than the notch duration. Basically, the problem was that this power-off circuit was being fooled into thinking the power had gone off. Interestingly enough, the young engineers who designed the circuit thought I was crazy for suggesting this, and told me so in no uncertain terms. Yet this is a problem I have seen at least a dozen times. Not only are these circuits often fooled by notches, but they can also be fooled by transients of one kind or another.

In another case, a department moved to a new location within a large building. They had been close to the computer room before and as a result were able to share power from the room which was supported by a 3000 kVA UPS. When they moved to the new location, they were no longer supported by the UPS but were on utility power. They were experiencing a number of problems—digital clocks running fast, network hub problems, and a host of other problems including a laser printer that was failing.

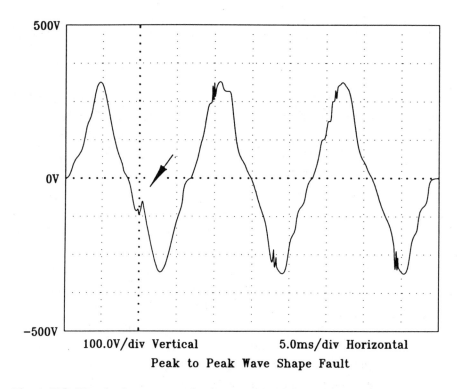

100.0V/div Vertical   5.0ms/div Horizontal

Peak to Peak Wave Shape Fault

Figure 7-8. *The check sorter at a bank processing facility had an SCR front end. The arrow shows the check sorter starting. Phase control notches appear thereafter.* (From BMI 4800)

The failed part in the laser printer was a special resistor that controlled current feeding the drum heater. The resistor was getting hot and burning up. Naturally, the sine wave had obvious notches. What was happening was that the printer used the zero crossing of the voltage sine wave. Since there were many zero crossings, the laser printer was cycling far more often than normal and the resistor was forced to stay on much longer than the duty cycle for which it was designed, causing it to overheat and fail.

In another part of the same building, the notches were fooling yet another power sensing circuit. This one was inside a brand new copier. It was interpreting the notches as a problem with RMS voltage, and as a result, it was refusing to operate. The source of the notching was the huge UPS *(Figure 7-9)*. It had a six pulse rectifier front end that was disturbing the voltage waveform coming from the utility transformer.

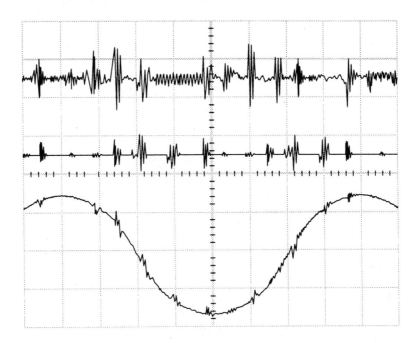

Figure 7-9. *This shows the notching caused by the large UPS. Notice that while the notches are clearly visible, it is doubtful that this oscilloscope captured the entire notch depth. Also, the other two traces show normal mode (line to neutral) and common mode (neutral to ground) noise associated with the notching.*

Notches are very fast and steep events. Don't be surprised if a power monitor or digital storage scope shows the notching to be relatively mild. Oftentimes, an instrument will be unable to capture an event like this and display the full extent of it. You can assume that any notch probably crosses the zero line even if it appears not to. Actually, notch depth is a function of the distribution system. The farther from the source of the notching, the smaller the notch (*Figure 7-10*). The notch depth at C will be 100% while the notch depth at points B and A will be 66% and 33%, respectively. Bear in mind that notch width increases as notch depth decreases.

Other problems I have seen include cross-talk between SCR rectified equipment sharing the same bus, general synchronization problems due to false zero crossings, emergency generators with regulators that cannot cope with the false crossings, UPSs that oscillate output voltage, and clocks that run fast.

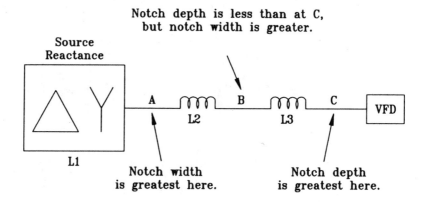

Figure 7-10. *If the source reactance and the two line reactances are equal, then the notch depth would be 100% at C, 66% at B, and 33% at A. As reactance is added, depth decreases and width increases.*

Fixing Notches

The secret to getting rid of line notching is line reactance. In *Figure 7-10*, we saw that the further away from the source of the notches we are, the less severe the notch depth, and the less severe the notch depth, the lower the voltage THD. Logic would lead us to the conclusion that if L2 were of sufficient impedance, other devices connected to the power source would not "see" any notching. In fact, if inductive reactance is added upstream, we can cure the notching problem.

This is not to say that any arbitrary value of reactance will do. As the impedance of L2 is increased, at some point voltage regulation to the power converter will be sacrificed, so picking the right value for line reactance that will clean up the notches and still provide proper voltage levels is a design goal.

It may have crossed your mind that if reactance is such a cure-all for notching, why is it that drive manufacturers and others don't include sufficient reactance in their product to eliminate the problem? Some do, many don't, and the reason is cost. Plus, notching won't necessarily be a problem in every facility, so manufacturers gamble, and if called for, they install an external line reactor to clean things up.

There are several commercially available ways to add line reactance. The first is from commercially manufactured line reactors. These are inductors that look much like L2 in *Figure 7-10*. Another method is to install an isolation transformer.

Isolation Transformers

Isolation transformers are especially useful when addressing line notching, when voltage transformation must take place to serve the power conversion equipment. The number one consideration becomes the leakage inductance of the primary. This is what provides the reactance to clean up the notching. However, we must be aware that higher frequency harmonics will cause core losses and eddy currents. This means we may need to look at a special transformer called a "K-factor" transformer. We will address this in a future chapter.

Line Reactors

When voltage transformation is not required, reactors are used to provide the inductive reactance needed to address notching. The most economic design type is a three phase iron core unit using laminated steel in the core and either copper or aluminum wire. The unit is mounted in an enclosure appropriate for the environment in which it is to operate. Line reactors are commercially available from drive manufacturers as accessories, or from third party sources specializing in such.

Diodes and THD

We've spent a lot of time talking about SCRs, yet there are many three phase power converters that use diodes in the bridge rectifier instead of SCRs. The natural commutation process of diodes eliminates the notching difficulties associated with forced commutation of SCRs because at the commutation instant, the voltage differential is zero. But as with the switch-mode power supplies we saw earlier, three phase diode bridges use capacitors in a fashion similar to single phase designs. This results in high peak capacitor charging currents. The crest factor and the ratio of peak to RMS current of a three phase diode bridge can be as high as 3 to 1. The result is flat topping of the voltage waveform in a fashion similar to those examples shown earlier.

The result of all this is that diode bridges can have just as much THD as SCR bridges, but they usually have somewhat less. The big advantage is that there isn't any notching of the voltage waveform. The dominant harmonics of a three-phase, six-pulse diode bridge are 5, 7, and 11. There are some higher order harmonics but not nearly as significant as those present when using SCRs.

8 Harmonics and Resonance

Figure 8-1a shows the current signature of a rectifier. This is just one of three phases, but notice the harmonic analysis (*Figure 8-1b*). Gone is the dreaded third harmonic. The bulk of the current is made up of the fifth and the seventh harmonics. This is indicative of a 6 pulse rectifier. Notice that 6 lies between 5 and 7. If this had been a 12 pulse rectifier, we would have seen large quantities of the eleventh and thirteenth harmonics and almost nothing below that. Like everything else, there is a mathematical explanation behind this, but what we really need to know is the effect of these harmonic currents.

The first thing that is obvious is that 5, 7, 11, and 13 are significantly higher numbers than 3. What this means is that the frequency of current flow at those harmonics is much higher than that of the third harmonic. Therefore, the heating

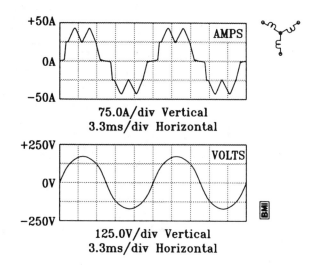

Figure 8-1a. *The voltage and current waveforms of a three phase computer power supply...*

		Jan 10 1992 (Fri)
Phase A Current Spectrum		8:55:29 AM
Fundamental amps:		82.5 A rms
Fundamental freq:		60.0 Hz

HARM	PCT	SINE PHASE	HARM	PCT	SINE PHASE
FUND	100.0%	-4°	2nd	0.2%	-59°
3rd	1.5%	69°	4th		
5th	28.0%	143°	6th		
7th	8.0%	-113°	8th		
9th	0.7%	55°	10th		
11th	5.1%	-32°	12th		
13th	3.9%	-34°	14th		
15th	0.4%	-180°	16th		
17th	3.5%	111°	18th		
19th	3.2%	120°	20th		
21st	0.4%	-57°	22nd		
23rd	2.9%	-98°	24th		
25th	2.1%	-90°	26th		
27th	0.2%	97°	28th		
29th	2.1%	48°	30th		
31st	1.6%	44°	32nd		
33rd	0.1%	-154°	34th		
35th	1.6%	-169°	36th		
37th	1.4%	-166°	38th		
39th	0.3%	-28°	40th		
41st	1.7%	-49°	42nd		
43rd	1.9%	-42°	44th		
45th	0.6%	102°	46th		
47th	1.2%	41°	48th		
49th	1.3%	56°	50th		
ODD	30.8%		EVEN	0.3%	
THD:	30.8%				

Figure 8-1b. *...along with current harmonic analysis.*

due to the skin effect, eddy currents, and other losses that were discussed earlier is even greater at these frequencies. Also, if you compare the analysis in *Figure 8-1b* with that of the pulse current in *Figure 3-3*, we see that we have substantially higher order harmonics in the current waveform of three phase power converters. This brings back all of the concerns expressed in earlier chapters except hot neutrals.

Resonance

What does resonance have to do with harmonics? Many of us were first exposed to the concept of resonance when we studied radio principles. The definition of resonance is when capacitive reactance equals inductive reactance ($2\pi fL = \frac{1}{2\pi fC}$). Reducing this equation will give us the resonant frequency given the known values of capacitive and inductive reactance yields $f_r = \frac{1}{2 \cdot \pi \cdot \sqrt{LC}}$.

Okay, so we know what resonance is—so what? Before we get to the "so what," we must take another look at harmonic current flow. Earlier, we stated that the non-linear load acts as a current generator at the harmonic frequencies and that these harmonics flow back toward the utility source. They do this because the source impedance of the utility is low in comparison to all of the other possible paths. These other paths are various loads that are connected to the same power source transformer, and they have significantly higher impedance (*Figure 8-2*).

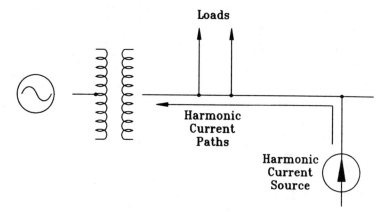

Figure 8-2. *Paradoxically, non-linear loads can be conceptualized as harmonic current generators that pump distorted current toward the utility source, even though all the current in the system loops between the source and the load just like it does at 60 Hz.*

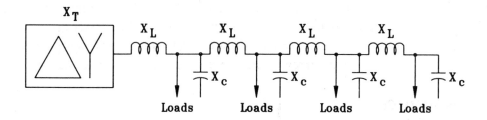

Figure 8-3. *The typical electrical distribution system as series inductance and parallel capacitance.*

Now let's look at the typical system of a building from an X_L and X_C standpoint (*Figure 8-3*). You can see that it can be electrically reduced to a number of series inductive reactances and shunt capacitive reactances. This is a result of power cable capacitance and inductance, in addition to actual discreet loads that are either inductive or capacitive in nature.

Now let's put a non-linear device on one end as a shunt device (*Figure 8-4*). Harmonic current now flows toward all of the X_Ls and X_Cs, in addition to the transformer X_t. It's easy to see (without doing a lot of higher mathematics) that the distribution system will have some natural resonant frequency.

The resistive elements in the circuits have little effect on resonance except to dampen the magnification of current and\or voltage that occurs when the natural resonance is excited. This amplification of harmonics due to resonance is the source of a variety of problems, including excessive currents, voltage, blown capacitor fuses, damaged capacitors, noise, and interference as a result of the amplified harmonics.

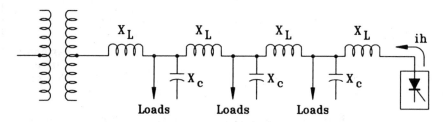

Figure 8-4. *The harmonic current flows toward the source and other loads. The frequency of current may excite resonance in some combination of Ls and Cs.*

Parallel Resonance

Parallel resonance (*Figure 8-5*) results when inductive reactance in the form of motors, in-house generation, and/or the utility transformer finds itself in parallel with power factor correction capacitors or other power system capacitance. Another term for a parallel resonant circuit is a "flywheel." If we excite a flywheel at the resonant frequency, the Ls and Cs will swap current back and forth, which sets up an oscillation at the resonant frequency. This oscillation produces voltage distortion which may cause harmonic currents to flow in other circuits.

Parallel resonant circuits are high impedance paths to non-linear load currents at the harmonic frequency, which creates increased harmonic voltages and high harmonic currents in each leg as the parallel impedance drops across them.

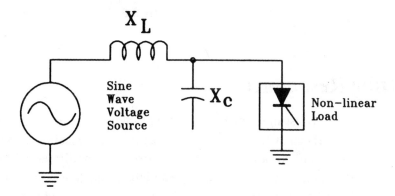

Figure 8-5. *Parallel Resonance.*

Series Resonance

If feeder capacitor banks appear to be in series with system inductances, a series resonant circuit can result (*Figure 8-6*). Series resonant circuits are a low impedance path to harmonic current—nearly a short circuit. That is why so many fuses across power factor correction capacitors blow when a new VFD is added to the load side. Suddenly a new harmonic current source is generating at a frequency that "sees" the shunt capacitor as a low impedance path. This is a typical example of series resonance.

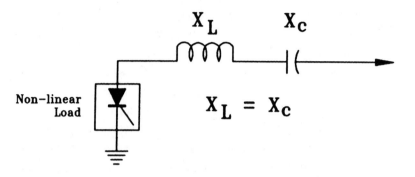

Figure 8-6. *Series Resonance.*

Spotting Resonance

Most significant resonance problems result from a large capacitor bank that has been installed, usually by the utility, to assist in voltage regulation and/or displacement power factor correction. Normally the resonant frequency of the system's inductive reactance and the capacitive reactance of the cap bank occur near the fifth or seventh harmonic. Resonance problems at the eleventh and thirteenth harmonics, however, are not unusual.

Utility capacitors are not the only problem. When a number of smaller capacitor banks are applied throughout the distribution system, there may be a number of different resonant frequencies, although in these cases, the resonant effect will be somewhat less than that of one large resonant element. The concern with series resonant conditions is that high capacitor currents can flow for relatively low harmonic voltages. In other words, capacitor failure is often a sign of series resonance. Parallel resonance is characterized by low current flow at the harmonics of interest while high voltage harmonics are present at the resonant frequency. The only way to verify this is to do both current and voltage harmonic analysis at various points in the system. The presence of resonance will generally appear as a larger-than-normal reading at the resonant frequency along the harmonic spectrum (*Figures 8-7a* and *8-7b*).

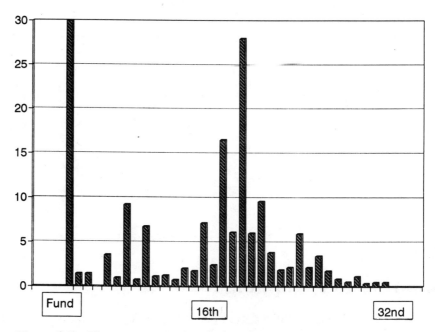

Figure 8-7a. *The current spectrum from series resonance will show unusually high readings at higher frequencies...*

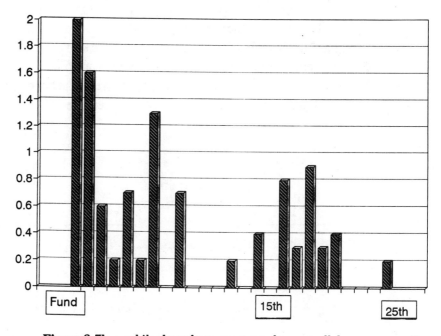

Figure 8-7b. *...while the voltage spectrum from parallel resonance will show similar groupings.*

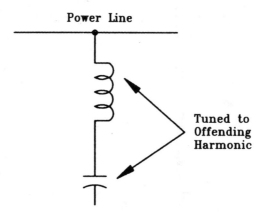

Figure 8-8. *A shunt filter.*

Shunting and Trapping Resonance

The preferred method of dealing with harmonic current generated by non-linear loads is through the use of filters. The basic function of a filter is to reduce or enhance the flow of harmonic current in the critical circuit. As we have seen, harmonic currents loop between the non-linear load and the power source. In general, most harmonic problems are the result of harmonic currents flowing in too long a path through too much impedance. We know from an earlier chapter that this is what causes voltage distortion. When harmonic currents flow along a long path, coupling—either inductive or capacitive—can be the source of electrical or telecommunications systems noise and interference.

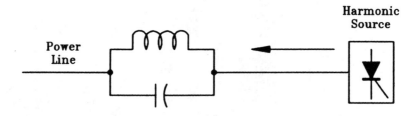

Figure 8-9. *A trap filter reduces current at the resonant frequency of the filter.*

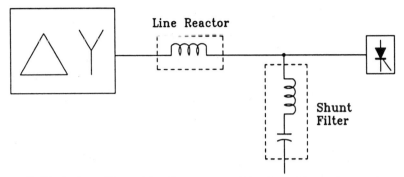

Figure 8-10. *A shunt filter with a line reactor. The shunt filter enhances harmonic current at the filter's frequency.*

A filter either diverts these currents through a shorter path or blocks the flow of current in the critical path. These two approaches are accomplished with either shunt filters or trap filters. A shunt filter (*Figure 8-8*) looks exactly like the series resonant circuit shown in *Figure 8-6*, except the circuit is made of discreet components rather than the random reactances of the facility. At the harmonic frequency, the filter looks like a short circuit, thereby diverting current through it and back to the harmonic current source—the non-linear load. A trap filter (*Figure 8-9*) looks similar to the parallel resonant circuit shown in *Figure 8-5*. This filter looks like a large impedance at the harmonic frequency for which it was designed, thereby blocking the flow of current at that frequency.

Filters come in many varieties, and one of the first decisions that must be made is whether or not the filter must address more than one harmonic frequency. If so, it is called a multistage filter. Then there are high-pass and low-pass filters. As the names imply, they are designed to be a low impedance path above or below the filter's cutoff point and to attenuate frequencies below or above the design frequency limits. Usually, the filter is placed near the non-linear load.

Sometimes it is possible to add a shunt filter to a line reactor to solve both notching and harmonic current flow (*Figure 8-10*). In addition, inductive reactance can be added to existing capacitors to detune the system away from the frequency at which currents are flowing in resonant paths within the facility. Applying filters is as much an art as it is a science. There are many factors to be considered, including the care it takes to insure that the new filter is not the source of some new resonance.

9 K-factor Transformers

We have referred several times to various losses experienced by transformers and the distribution system in general, due to the heating effects of harmonics. In a transformer there are always I^2R losses. What this means is that when DC or AC current is passed through any transformer, the resistance of the windings themselves will produce a loss proportional to the resistance times the square of the current.

In the real world of building power, we are not too concerned with DC current because we use AC current. When AC current is passed through a transformer, losses are produced. Transformer losses include DC and AC resistance in the winding, eddy currents in the windings and core, and hysteresis losses in the core. All other losses are called stray losses. An eddy current is produced by the voltage induced by the magnetic field that surrounds each winding conductor and all other metal material permeated by the field. These eddy currents must be dissipated as heat by the windings and associated insulating materials.

What's important to know about eddy current losses is that they are proportional to the square of the AC frequency. Knowing this, we can immediately understand the problem of transformers and harmonic currents. The problem becomes more complicated when we consider the reality that non-linear currents are apt to be the sum of many harmonics. In order to determine the actual losses, we must total the sum of the losses associated with currents calculated at each frequency.

$$\text{Irms} = \sqrt{(\text{Ih}_1)^2 + (\text{Ih}_2)^2 + (\text{Ih}_3)^2 + ...(\text{Ih}_n)^2}$$

Figure 9-1. *Equation for true RMS current.*

$$\% \text{ I p.u.} = (\frac{Ih_n}{I_{Total}})$$

Figure 9-2. *Percent per unit calculation, given total RMS or peak reference value.*

Where Does K-factor Come From?

The equation in *Figure 9-1* shows us how to calculate total true RMS current given the harmonic currents. Once we have the total, we can calculate the percent current per unit for each harmonic (*Figure 9-2*). This will yield a number less than one so that when all are added up, we will get a total of one, or one unit.

The landmark work on this method is ANSI/IEEE C57.110-1986. We will take the example from that publication and use it to see how these calculations lead us to K-factor, though the IEEE standard never uses the term "K-factor."

In the example, they use a 1200 amp transformer having a non-linear load with the harmonic content and per unit load current, as shown in *Figure 9-3*. They ask us to determine the maximum load current under these circumstances. This is where we must diverge from the standard and find out about "K-factor."

h_n	$I_h(pu)$
1	0.978
5	0.171
7	0.108
11	0.044
13	0.028
17	0.015
19	0.0098

Figure 9-3. *Load currents from example in IEEE C57.110*

$$K = \sum_{n=1}^{n=\infty} [(\text{Ih}_{n(\text{pu})})^2 h_n^2]$$

Figure 9-4. *K-factor equation.*

The standard defines the mathematical process for determining K but never names K, or K-factor. The use of the term "K" came about through procedures used by Underwriter's Laboratory (UL) along with transformer manufacturers. As a result, we now have the formula shown in *Figure 9-4*.

While this may look somewhat daunting, all it really tries to do is to account for the heating effects of current in the transformer. (Σ) means to sum all of the values found by doing the operation to the right of sigma, so we square each of the per unit harmonic currents and multiply the harmonic number squared. Bear in mind that since we are using per unit values, we will always end up with numbers that are less than one.

When we add up the results of these individual calculations, we find the K-factor. In this case, it is 2.729. What this means is very important—there will be 2.729 times as much heat produced by the non-linear current than would have been produced by the same RMS value of linear current!

The remainder of the calculation shown in the standard relates to derating an existing transformer. To use this part of the calculation we must know the transformer kVA rating, the primary winding resistance, the secondary winding resistance, and load loss under rated conditions. A number of software programs and/or spread sheet templates are available to help us plug in the numbers and get the maximum permissible load current with the given harmonic composition. In the case presented in the standard, the given harmonic content resulted in derating the transformer by about 10%, therefore limiting the load current to about 1084 amps.

$$K = \frac{\sum[f_h^2 h^2]}{\sum[f_h^2]}$$

Figure 9-5. *Harmonic Distribution Factor equation.*

Harmonic Distribution Factor

ANSI/IEEE describes another method of calculating K-factor called the Harmonic Distribution Factor. This is shown in *Figure 9-5*. Notice, however, that instead of using "I" current we now use "f" factor instead. If we look at *Figure 9-6*, we see a comparison of the two methods. At a glance, the difference is obvious. The first "I" method uses the actual per unit value of current while the Harmonic Distribution Factor method expresses each harmonic as a percent of the fundamental current. The K-factor calculated using either method yields the same number.

These two methods of arriving at K-factor relate to the two most popular harmonic analyzers on the market. Dranetz Corporation measures the current at each harmonic frequency. This enables the operator to use the first method of calculating K-factor. BMI, on the other hand, expresses each harmonic as a percent of the fundamental. These numbers fit into the harmonics distribution factor equation to arrive at K-factor. It should be noted that either way is just as accurate and efficient in assisting the operator in the analysis process.

K-FACTOR CALCULATION					K-FACTOR CALCULATION					
h_n	$I_h(pu)$	$I_h(pu)^2$	h_n^2	$[I_h(pu)^2 h_n^2]$	h_n	$\% f_h$	f_h	f_h^2	h_n^2	$[f_h^2 h_n^2]$
1	0.978	0.95700	1	0.957	1	100.0	1.0000	1.0000	1	1.0000
5	0.171	0.02900	25	0.731	5	17.5	0.1750	0.0360	25	0.7650
7	0.108	0.01200	49	0.571	7	11.0	0.1100	0.0122	49	0.5978
11	0.044	0.00200	121	0.234	11	4.5	0.0450	0.0020	121	0.2420
13	0.028	0.00078	169	0.133	13	2.9	0.0209	0.0008	169	0.1352
17	0.015	0.00023	289	0.065	17	1.5	0.0150	0.0002	289	0.0578
19	0.0098	0.00010	381	0.038	19	1.0	0.0100	0.0001	381	0.0361
$\Sigma = 1.00$ $\Sigma = K = 2.7$					$\Sigma = 1.0459$ $\Sigma = 2.8339$					

$$K = \frac{\Sigma[f_h^2 h_n^2]}{\Sigma[f_h^2]} = \frac{2.8339}{1.0459} = 2.7$$

[f_h = Harmonic Distribution Factor]

Figure 9-6. *Comparison of the two methods for calculating K-factor.*

What are K-factor Transformers?

It is important to point out that our purpose here is not to derate three phase transformers that support non-linear loads. This should only be done by qualified engineers using precise information from manufacturers and only in rare circumstances. Normally, K-factor comes into play during the design and installation phase of a project, and K-factor calculations are used as a specification criteria for new or replacement power source equipment. The important point to note here is that K-factor relates to the excessive heat that must be dissipated. It represents a multiple of the heating that can be expected by the same magnitude of current at the fundamental power frequency. The thing to do with the K-factor calculation is to round up to the nearest whole number, so a K 2.75 becomes a K 3. You may find that most manufacturers do not make a K 3 transformer, and that K 4 is the next rating (*Figure 9-7*).

Typical loads like PCs, drives, and UPSs have predictable characteristics and related K-ratings for transformers that can support them. *Figure 9-8* shows a list of transformer loads and a conservative estimate of the K-rating the supply transformer should have. All regular transformers are K 1 but are not rated as such by a listing agency. On the other hand, to become a K-rated transformer, UL tests the unit to meet the special heat dissipation requirement associated with the K-rating, and UL requires a 200% neutral rating. The listing label carries the following notation: "Suitable For Non-Sinusoidal Current Load with a K-factor Not to Exceed _____." The manufacturer then inserts the appropriate K-rating number.

Commercially Available K-rated Transformers
K - 4
K - 9
K - 13
K - 20
K - 30
K - 40

Figure 9-7. *Typical commercially available K-rated transformers.*

Load	K-factor
Incandescent lighting (with no solid state dimmers)	K-1
Electric resistance heating (with no solid state heat controls)	K-1
Motors (without solid state drives)	K-1
Control transformers/electromadnetic control devices	K-1
Motor-generators (without solid state drives)	K-1
Electric-discharge lighting	K-4
UPS w/optional input filtering	K-4
Welders	K-4
Induction heating equipment	K-4
PLCs and solid state controls (other than variable speed drives)	K-4
Telecommunications equipment (e.g. PBX)	K-13
UPS without input filtering	K-13
Multiwire receptacle circuits in general care areas of health care, facilities and classrooms of schools, etc.	K-13
Multiwire receptacle circuits supplying inspection or testing equipment on an assembly or production line	K-13
Mainframe computer loads	K-20
Solid state motor drives (variable speed drives)	K-20
Multiwire receptacle circuits in critical care areas and operating/recovery rooms of hospitals	K-20
Multiwire receptacle circuits in industrial, medical, and educational laboratories	K-30
Multiwire receptacle circuits in commercial office spaces	K-30
Small mainframes (mini and micro)	K-30
Other loads identified as producing very high amounts of harmonics (especially in higher orders)	K-40

Figure 9-8. *These are only estimates. Unless a designer is familiar with the exact loads, a harmonic analysis of the equipment should be done before determining K-factor.*

From this we might infer that a K-rated and safety listed transformer is specially designed and constructed. This may or may not be true. What it does mean is that the submitted device has passed rigorous testing criteria not applied to standard transformers by UL. This may have been accomplished by submitting an oversized transformer for testing, and noting where it passed the tests for a given K-factor rating at a given kVA.

Many have complained that some K-rated 100 kVA transformers are nothing more than 150 kVA transformers in disguise. Some manufacturers, however, do special things to their transformers to handle the harmonic heat. This may include special windings, insulation, and/or core material. Let the buyer beware!

Typical K-rated transformers are 600V ventilated, dry-types. Most are Delta/Wye wound and come in temperature ratings of 150°C, 115°C, and 80°C. A 220°C UL component recognized insulation system is used in most units.

To deal with the eddy current losses and skin effect of harmonic heating, the primary and secondary windings use smaller-than-normal, paralleled, individually insulated, and transposed conductors. If a high percentage of third harmonic is expected, the Delta windings will be sized according to limit temperature rise. Also, the secondary neutral must be oversized to twice the ampacity of the phase conductors.

In this book, the term "total harmonic distortion" has been used. Intuitively we might guess that the larger the THD of the load, the greater the K-factor. This would be correct. The real question that needs to be asked is, "Do I need a larger K-rating for PC loads or VFDs?"

The answer can be seen in *Figure 9-9*. Frequency has a dramatic effect on K-factor, and THD does not. Notice that the K-factor of 100% THD of the third harmonic is five, while the K-factor of only 20% THD of the thirteenth harmonic is more than seven.

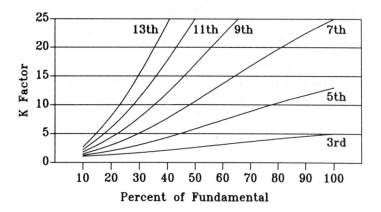

Figure 9-9. *This chart shows the effects of different harmonics on K-factor. Notice that K-factor is much more dependent on frequency than on THD.*

The Liabilities

What if we ignore the whole issue of K-factor transformers? What are the implications? There are several. Obviously, transformer failure is right at the top of the list.

The biggest expected consequence of transformer failure is downtime. It may take several days or weeks to find a replacement transformer. They are heavy and are usually installed in places where ease of replacement was never planned. It is not unusual to have to remove walls, windows, or concrete. If the transformer supported a critical application like a computer room or telecommunications closet, the very existence of the business entity could be jeopardized. Of course, the hard cost of downtime is not insignificant in any case.

It is rare for a transformer failure to become the source of a building fire, but a transformer failure is not a pretty thing. Normally the damage due to smoke can be just as threatening as any fire, and transformers that fail have a tendency to produce enormous amounts of toxic smoke.

But beyond all of the obvious physical and financial problems is the liability involved. Should a transformer failure result in litigation, it is the subject of debate as to whether the transformer manufacturer or user would be held liable. If the transformer is UL listed but not K-rated, and the load is non-linear, who stands behind the product? Good question. It would seem obvious that the manufacturer could make a good argument as to the extent of their liability. Ultimately it will land in the lap of the user to prove that the electrical infrastructure was specified to support known electrical loads. K-factor could easily be the determining factor in the extent of liability in a disaster from a failing transformer.

Finally, there is the issue of criminal liability. If management knowingly ignores a potential safety hazard and injuries result, can management can be sent directly to jail? In California, the answer is yes. As we stated earlier, it's the law (SB 6320).

10 Worldwide Standards, Measuring, and Analysis

Standards-creating bodies have not been idle while non-linear loads have proliferated. Since the early 1970s, power systems engineers have had a growing level of concern. These groups have turned to legislation and regulation to force the change in harmonics levels produced by equipment. This was necessitated since no economic incentives were available to provide designers with the motivation to build less offensive systems. The objectives of power engineers from the U.S.A. and Europe has had two common themes: first, to preserve the sinusoidal nature of the power systems voltage waveform; second, to protect the power system and its components from the effects of harmonic current loading. Interestingly enough, the Americans and Europeans have chosen two completely different yet complimentary approaches to the problem. The two efforts resulted in standards designed to limit harmonics: IEEE-519 and IEC-555 part 2.

The earliest efforts came from Europe. In 1969, both the European Committee for Electrotechnical Standardization and IEC (International Electrotechnical Commission) formed committees to address harmonic issues relating to home appliances. The first standard was announced in 1975 and was adopted by fourteen European countries. By 1982, the Germans led the way toward a more comprehensive document called IEC-555-2. Recently this standard has been revised and includes not only household appliances but nearly all electrical loads and establishes stringent limits as to current distortion by device.

Meanwhile, the Industry Applications Society of IEEE began work on harmonic standards in 1973 and a "Guide" 519 was delivered in 1981. In 1986, this guide was upgraded in status to that of "Recommended Practice." It eventually became known as ANSI/IEEE "Standard" 519-1992, and was greatly expanded.

IEC-555

What makes IEC-555 so important is that in order for any manufacturer to do business with the European community, their equipment must meet the standard by 1995. For this reason, IEC-555 has the weight of a worldwide standard and probably will force changes in power supply design that is shipped worldwide by major manufacturers. The standard covers four classes of equipment from 220-415 and 0-16 amps per phase:

Class A: Balanced three phase equipment and all other equipment except stated in Classes B, C, and D.

Class B: Portable tools.

Class C: Lighting equipment including dimming devices.

Class D: Equipment having an input current with a "special wave shape," as defined by *Figure 10-1*, except those covered by Classes B and C and motor driven equipment.

Figure 10-1 should look familiar to us since it deals with those diode capacitor input power supplies we talked about earlier. The Class D standard outlines current limits that must be met (*Figure 10-2*).

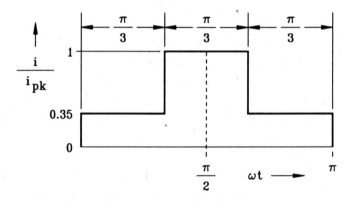

Figure 10-1. *Current with a special wave shape, IEC-555.*

IEEE-519

The 519 standard takes a different approach. While the Europeans worry about individual pieces of equipment, IEEE-519 worries about the levels of harmonics at the PCC (Point of Common Coupling) or Utility Service Entrance. The approach layed out in the standard is to limit a customer's current distortion based

Harmonic	Maximum permissible harmonic current	
order n	relative limits (mA/W)	absolute limits (A)
Odd harmonics		
3	3.6	1.08
5	2.0	0.60
7	1.5	0.45
9	1.0	0.30
$11 \leq n \leq 39$	0.6x11/n	0.18x11/n
Even harmonics		
2	1.0	0.3
.4	0.5	0.15

Figure 10-2. *Proposed Class D standard current limits for IEC-555.*

on the relative size of the load and the supply voltage distortion based on the voltage level. Please note that the standard does not apply to individual pieces of equipment except to the extent that they contribute to distortion at the service entrance. *Figure 10-3* shows the limits for voltage distortion for given voltage levels, and *Figure 10-4* shows the allowable levels of current distortion at the below 69 kV level. Note that the categories are defined by the ratio of the load at the fundamental to the short circuit current available at the PCC.

Bus voltage at PCC	Individual voltage distortion (%)	Total voltage distortion (%)
Below 69 kV	3.0	5.0
69 kV to 138 kV	1.5	2.5
138 kV and above	1.0	1.5

Figure 10-3. *Proposed IEEE-519 voltage distortion limits.*

Maximum Harmonic Current Distribution in % of Fundamental						
Harmonic Order (Odd Harmonics)						
I_{sc}/I_L	h<11	11≤h<17	17≤h<23	23≤h<35	35≤h	
<20*	4.0	2.0	1.5	0.6	0.3	5.0
20-50	7.0	3.5	2.5	1.0	0.5	8.0
50-100	10.0	4.5	4.0	1.5	0.7	12.0
100-1000	12.0	5.5	5.0	2.0	1.0	15.0
>1000	15.0	7.0	6.0	2.5	1.4	20.0
Even harmonics are limited to 25% of the odd harmonic limits above.						
*All power generation equipment is limited to these values of current distortion, regardless of actual I_{sc}/I_L.						
Where I_{sc} = Maximum short circuit current at PCC. and I_L = Maximum load current (fundamental frequency) at PCC.						

Figure 10-4. *Proposed IEEE-519 current distortion limits below 69 kV.*

Compatible Standards?

IEEE-519 is concerned with system-wide harmonics and how it effects the utility interface. The standard acknowledges that the utility does not have an unlimited capacity to absorb user-generated harmonic currents. The limits on harmonics attempt to prevent users from using up the utilities capacity and reducing voltage distortion problems. While these limits seem straightforward, they have spawned a number of legitimate concerns voiced by those trying to meet the standards. For instance, what is the available short circuit current at the PCC, and what is the maximum fundamental load current? Some loads have varying harmonic levels, and system-wide harmonics can be dynamic as well. What does the standard say about that? What about on-site generators? And what happens to short circuit current when the utility undergoes switching operations?

For the system designer, these questions directly affect compliance. It is for this reason that harmonic measurement and analysis is vital. Compliance without direct measurement is risky. Then there are the effects of the mix of harmonic loads either within a facility or between facilities sharing the same PCC. Determining harmonic current flow in complex systems is no easy task. Electrical systems are dynamic, so establishing harmonic limits at one point of the system is not practical for the designer who may not be able to ensure compliance after the fact.

IEC-555, on the other hand, attempts to decrease harmonic current at every device. This seems laudable at first glance, but unless it can be applied equally and all at once, we can predict some undesirable results. It should be noted that it will take many years after IEC-555 requirements become mandatory before significant harmonic reductions are realized. This is because of the large numbers of devices installed at present facilities that were not manufactured to meet the standard.

Let's assume for a moment that some of the non-linear devices in a building are suddenly replaced with power factor connected units. For a time, harmonic distortion may increase significantly on a system-wide basis. How can that be? A by-product of the previous mix of harmonic loads may have been harmonic current cancellation. This cancellation would have been lost with the replacement of the older devices. In fact, PCs and some other harmonic loads may have an electrical symbiotic relationship as their currents blend and cancel in the complex flow of power through common elements of the distribution system.

Clearly these two standards are well thought out and are needed steps toward a cleaner electrical environment, but all is not as simple as it first seems. Creating standards will be an ongoing process as we learn more about the dynamics of devices, distribution systems, and utility interface.

Harmonic Measurement and Analysis

The number of products available for harmonic measurement and analysis is growing about as fast as the level of awareness of harmonics as a power quality issue. A few years ago, the only products available for this purpose were large, complex instruments which cost well over $10,000. While these devices where excellent, the cost and complexity often restricted access to the technology. As a result, ignorance of the topic and of site problems persisted.

Today, many hand-held units have recently become available that give most of the critical information a practitioner would need to decide if further investigation with more complex apparatus would yield results. But the need for measurement and analysis is more fundamental than trying to pick out a fancy box to buy. As I have travelled across the country teaching and speaking, I have posed many questions to the audience, such as, "If you were directed to measure the load on a given transformer, where would you take the measurement?" Or, "What instrument would you use to take the measurement?" The answers vary from group to group. However, a large percentage of truly honest respondents unfortunately state that they would take their meter and go to the primary side of the transformer and not the secondary.

For those of us who make a living debating the fine points of clock speed and band width, the answer may seem amusing, but think of the electrician who has been issued a volt/ohm meter with a clamp-on current probe that he knows nothing about. No one has bothered to tell him about non-linear loads or proper measuring equipment. It is the people doing the measuring that need support and educational resources, and it is at this fundamental level that the discussion of measurement and analysis needs to focus.

True RMS vs. Alternatives

The waveform of voltage and current has long been assumed to be sinusoidal and fundamental. Therefore, most measuring equipment has been designed with these pure waves in mind. But as we have seen throughout this book, many waveforms that we want to measure are not even close to sinusoidal. These unexpected waveforms can trick some meters into giving results that contain rather large errors.

Two common metering techniques involve looking for the average or the peak of the voltage or current. The most inexpensive digital voltmeters use a form of averaging to produce readings. Since RMS = 1.11 times average, these meters look at the instantaneous voltage over a cycle, do a simple calculation, and display the result. Peak reading meters look for the highest instantaneous voltage and multiply that by .707.

Of course, the problem is obvious. Both of these types of meters anticipate the waveform to be that of a pure sine wave. The constants of .707 and 1.11 give consistent results with the actual RMS (root of the mean of the square) value only for a pure sine wave. True RMS digital meters sample the input at a high rate about 100 times the input frequency and convert these time slices into samples. A microprocessor squares each sample and sums the square along with those of each previous sample, then takes the square root of the sum. This method gives a precise calculation of true RMS regardless of the distortion of the wave shape being measured.

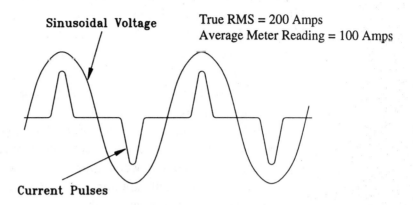

Figure 10- 5. *This familiar pulse current signature must be measured with a "true RMS" meter. Cheap averaging meters could give a reading of only half of the actual current!*

It should be noted that the most common meter among electricians today is an average reading RMS calibrated meter. If we look at the familiar pulse current signature of a switching power supply (*Figure 10-5*), a true RMS meter would give us an accurate reading. An averaging meter would read only about half as much, so if we measure neutral current with the wrong meter, we are liable to believe we don't have a problem at 12 amps when the true RMS current on that branch circuit neutral could be over 20 amps. The only proper meter to use to measure voltage and (especially) current is a true RMS meter. Anything else may be worse than taking no measurement at all.

Where to Measure

As mentioned earlier, a surprising number of electricians would go to the primary of a transformer instead of its secondary to measure its loading. The first challenge is to make sure the measurement is done with a true RMS meter. The second challenge is to take the measurement in the right place. We know that the third harmonic will circulate in the Delta winding of a transformer. We will not measure any of the current circulating in the transformer if we look at the primary. The secondary side will give us an accurate reading of the full load current, though.

In many cases, we will want to use an analyzer to look at the distortion of the current waveform or to do an actual harmonic analysis. In order to place the meter appropriately, we must think about what we are measuring. For instance, if the third harmonic is trapped in the delta winding, we won't get an accurate picture of load current on the primary side of the transformer. If we want to analyze the harmonic current of a given load—say a VFD—we should get on the input wires of the VFD. Should the VFD share a load center with other devices, looking at the input to the load center will give us the signature of everything fed from that panel board (*Figure 10-6*).

On the other hand, if we want to look at voltage distortion, we will want to place our meter at various points downstream from the power source. All of the loads that share the same power source transformer will "see" the same voltage distortion, as long as significant impedance is not presented by long runs of wire. Measuring points are interrelated to the relationship between voltage, impedance, and current. If we understand these elements with respect to the power distribution system, we will always understand where to take the measurements.

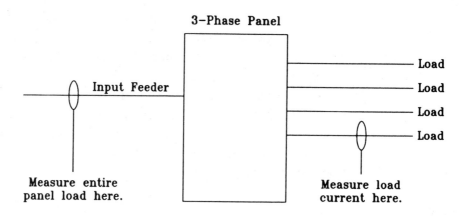

Figure 10-6. *To measure voltage and current and perform harmonic analysis, we must understand the relationship between voltage and current flow through the distribution system.*

The Need For Harmonic Analysis

Harmonic currents can create life/safety problems along with a variety of operational problems. The need for harmonic measurements and analysis has never been more important. Every facility should establish a program of regular measurement and monitoring. The variety of today's instruments allows maintenance personnel to do spot checks and then follow up with more sophisticated equipment for a full-blown analysis. In some facilities, permanent monitors should be installed for regular reporting. Often this can be combined with many other measurements including power demand (kW, power factor, kW hours) and power quality (impulses, outages, wave shape changes).

The Need for Education

Buying equipment for monitoring harmonics is only the beginning. The knowledge and know-how that go hand in hand with the investment are essential. Most of the analyzer manufacturers have excellent classes and resources that back up their products. They are not just in the business to sell boxes—they have an emotional investment in problem solving. Investing in classes and in an ongoing relationship with one or more of these companies is invaluable. Without this additional effort, many $10,000 instruments stay in closets and are never used for two basic reasons: first, personnel doesn't know how to use them, and second, they don't know what the output data means. Manufacturers' classes will easily remedy both of these weaknesses.

Another reason for education is that the topic of harmonics—along with power quality and power demand—is a growing, vital area of development. The body of knowledge is growing and the data base of expertise is expanding. Those of us involved in the educational effort are part of a network that users, practitioners, and electricians can tap into for faster answers and problem solving. In short, someone else has probably already had to deal with the same problem you are facing. Education not only provides answers, but access to the network of people who can make your next step in harmonics troubleshooting easier.

Conclusion

It's standard practice to build a building, move everyone in, and add loads forever and ever, amen. In many cases, the breakers in the electrical panels are never maintained or exercised. The loads are rarely measured, profiled, or analyzed. Minimal effort is spent on building upkeep. Facility managers, engineers, and maintenance professionals are often a low budgetary and operational priority. In short, we ignore the facility until something goes wrong or stops working, or a disaster happens.

When something does go wrong, we must strike while the iron is hot, so to speak, since upper management has a limited attention span. Two weeks after the event, memories begin to fade, priorities change, and panic gets replaced with an, "Oh, well, we'll get around to it," attitude. Of course, during the event, there was plenty of blaming, name calling, and finger pointing, to be sure. Oftentimes, a decision is made to buy something, anything—a black box to fix the problem. Throw enough money at a problem, and if it doesn't go away you can always blame the manufacturer or installer, and start the cycle all over again.

What this book has shown, beyond anything else, is that understanding the electrical environment is critical. The building distribution system is a dynamic, ever-changing thing, and it can't be left alone for years without careful study and attention. At the very least, proper electrical maintenance of breakers, connections, and critical systems should be performed one once a year. Each load center should be analyzed for power quality and harmonic content of both voltage and current. This information should be included in a profile of the department or workspace that is supported by the load center.

After a baseline has been established, new loads should be analyzed in relation to that baseline. Additions or changes—remodeling, new construction, or anything that changes the electrical environment —should be the impetus for a re-evaluation of the distribution system and the effects that may be felt locally or throughout the system.

Harmonic analysis and an understanding of how loads interact are essential to meet facility safety and operational standards, and should not be ignored or taken lightly. Harmonics is a subject that must be understood along with grounding, noise and surge suppression, lightning protection, and power quality concerns in general. Only in this context can problems related to harmonics be integrated into an overall plan to create an electrical environment that is friendly to sensitive loads and to people.

This book is only an introduction to the theory of harmonics, but it was never intended to be more than that. It's an overview of what harmonics are, how they make their appearance, what causes them, and some approaches to mitigate their effects. The reader now has two paths to follow: get more in-depth knowledge (if so desired), and/or integrate this overview into a broader understanding of power quality principles that go beyond harmonics.

I have a mental picture of an electrician or facility manager standing in front of an open electrical panel, scratching his head. Going through his mind are questions regarding harmonic current, ground loops, and voltage surges. As he looks over his shoulder, he sees a whole group of us asking the same questions. All of us have been there at one time or another.

At this point, I hope you can open this book and get answers to your questions, or at least eliminate some of the more puzzling options. After reading this book, you should know exactly what is and what is not related to harmonics, and how to proceed from there.

Good luck!

Glossary

Derating Factor: A number defined as (1.414) x average RMS phase current/ peak phase current. This factor, when applied to the rated load of a transformer, gives an indication as to the percent loading that is reasonable when that transformer must service nonlinear loads.

Diode/Capacitor Input: A power supply that uses a full wave bridge rectifier followed by a capacitor. This combination produces the characteristic pulse current signature.

Displacement Power Factor: The difference between apparent power and true power when only the phase relationship of voltage and current at the fundamental are taken into account.

Distortion Power Factor: The difference between apparent power and true power at all harmonic frequencies.

Distortion: Wave shape discontinuities.

Eddy Currents: Induced currents in transformer windings and core caused by harmonics.

Fast Fourier Transform (FFT): A set of algorithms that significantly shortens and simplifies the computation of a Fourier Series, and is typically implemented in microprocessor based sampling and measuring equipment that performs harmonic and spectral analysis.

Forced Commutation: The process of pulsing the gate on an SCR to force it to conduct current.

Forward Transfer Impedance: The ability of a source to provide harmonic current to a load.

Fourier's Transform: A type of mathematics that allows any waveform to be expressed as a series of sine waves at multiples of the fundamental period of the wave.

Full Wave Bridge Rectifier: An arrangement of power diodes that converts alternating current into pulsating direct current during 360° of the AC sine wave.

Fundamental Frequency: The rate at which alternating current cycles through 360° of rotation. 60 Hz, for example, means that there are sixty such 360° cycles during one second.

Gate Turn Off Thyristor (GTO): A unique type of SCR that can be switched on like an SCR with a positive gate pulse, but can also be switched off without power commutation circuits.

Harmonic: An integer multiple of the fundamental frequency.

Harmonic Analysis: The process of breaking down a complex waveform into a series of harmonics at various phase angles that describe the original waveform.

Harmonic Distortion: The mathematical representation of discontinuities in a pure sine waveform.

Harmonic Distribution Factor: A method of arriving at K-factor by using the fundamental current component as 100% and expressing the harmonics in relation to the fundamental.

Harmonic Frequencies: The harmonic times the fundamental frequency.

Hysteresis Losses: The energy used in the core of a transformer to overcome the residual magnetism left from the previous half cycle.

Integer Multiple: A whole number by which the fundamental is multiplied.

Internal Impedance: The ability of a source to provide current at its designed frequency (i.e. 60 Hz).

K-factor: A number based on the harmonic content of load current that determines the maximum safe loading on a power source.

K-rated Transformers: A transformer that is rated or designed to serve as the source for a predefined capacity of harmonic current.

Line Reactors: Inductance placed in series with a power converter-type load to eliminate notching of the source voltage waveform.

Natural Commutation: The process of allowing SCRs to turn on and off following the normal polarity of source voltage.

Negatively Sequenced: When the phases cross the zero line in ACB order instead of ABC.

Neutral Conductor: The grounded conductor that acts as the common return for load current.

Non-sinusoidal: Waveforms that do not look like sine waves.

Non-linear Loads: Loads that do not draw current in direct relationship to the voltage waveforms.

Notching: A sudden subcycle reversal of voltage to below or above the zero line, caused by a phase-to-phase short in SCR-type loads.

Output Impedance: The ability of a source to deliver current as seen from the load.

Parallel Resonance: A circuit where inductive reactance equals capacitive reactance and these circuit elements are connected in parallel.

Points of Common Coupling (PCC): The service entrance where building power is connected to utility power.

Power Factor Corrected Power Supplies (PFC): Those supplies that draw current in a more sinusoidal fashion rather than in current pulses that typify uncorrected switching power supplies.

Periodic Waveform: A waveform that repeats its cycles in a defined time at regular intervals.

Phase Conductors: Conductors that carry current from the output of a power source.

Phasor Rotation: The order in which waveforms from each successive phase cross zero.

Positively Sequenced: When each phase crosses zero in the order ABC.

Resonance: When capacitive reactance in a circuit equals inductive reactance in that same circuit.

SCR: Silicon Controlled Rectifier.

Sequencing: The order in which phases cross zero.

Series Resonance: A circuit where capacitive reactance equals inductive reactance and the circuit elements are in series.

Shunt Filter: A filter connected from one line to another designed to be a low impedance path at the frequency, or band of frequencies, of interest.

Sine Wave: A waveform that appears similar to the sine function in trigonometry

Sinusoidal: Looking like or having the qualities of a sine wave.

Skin Effect: The characteristic of power flow increasing near the outer area of a conductor as frequency is increased.

Switching or Switch-mode Power Supply: A power supply that converts AC power into high frequency DC power using a diode capacitor input and semiconductor switches.

Thyristor: Another term for SCR.

Total Harmonic Distortion (THD): A representation of the relative amount of harmonic content verses the fundamental of any waveform.

Transients: A subcycle disturbance of the AC waveform of a non periodic nature.

Trap Filter: A filter connected in series with the line that has a high impedance at the frequency, or band of frequencies, of interest.

Triplen Harmonics: Harmonics that are multiples of the third harmonic. Typically, only odd multiples of the third are included when the term is used.

Zero Sequenced: When all three phases cross zero at the same instant, they are zero sequenced.

Bibliography

J. Arrillaga; D. A. Bradley; P. S. Bodger. *Power System Harmonics*. New York, NY: John Wiley & Sons, 1985.

Basic Measuring Instruments. *Handbook of Power Signatures*: Second Edition. Santa Clara, CA, 1993.

Dorr, Douglas and Stanislawski, James. *A Unique Approach to Elimination of Harmonic Neutral Currents*. National Power Laboratory, [n.d.].

Dranetz Technologies, Inc. *Case Studies*. Edison, NJ, 1991.

Dranetz Technologies, Inc. *Power Line Harmonic Problems—Causes and Cures*. Edison, NJ, 1990.

Electric Power Research Institute. *Adjustable Speed Drives: Application Guide*. Pleasant Hill, CA: EPRI, 1992.

End-Use Power Line Harmonics (Course Text). Foster City, CA: BMI Advanced Power Quality Lab, 1990.

Frank, Jerry. "The How And Why Of K-factor Transformers." *EC&M* (May, 1993).

Freund, Arthur. "Double The Neutral and Derate The Transformer—Or Else." *EC&M* (December, 1988).

Freund, Arthur. "Non-linear Loads Mean Trouble." *EC&M* (March, 1988).

Gruzs, Thomas. "A Survey of Neutral Currents in Three-Phase Computer Power Systems." *IEEE Transactions on Industry Applications* (July/August, 1990).

IEEE Industry Applications Society/Power Engineering Society. *IEEE Std. 519-1992: IEEE Recommended Practices and Requirements for Harmonic Control in Electrical Systems.* New York, NY: Institute of Electrical and Electronic Engineers, 1993.

IEEE Power Engineering Society. *IEEE C57.110-1986: Recommended Practice for Establishing Transformer Capability When Supplying Nonsinusoidal Load Currents.* New York, NY: Institute of Electrical and Electronic Engineers, 1988.

IEEE Power Engineering Society. *IEEE Std. 1100-1992: Recommended Practice for Powering and Grounding Sensitive Electronic Equipment.* New York, NY: Institute of Electrical and Electronic Engineers, 1992.

John Fluke Mfg. Co., Inc. *In Tune With Power Harmonics.* Everett, WA, 1992.

Key, Eugene George. *Principles of Electricity.* New York, NY: Barnes & Noble Books, 1967.

Key, Tom and Lai, Jih-Sheng. *Comparison of Standards Limiting Harmonic Distortion in Power Systems.* Knoxville, TN: Reprint for IEEE 1991 Industrial Commercial Power Systems Technical Conference, [n.d.].

Kreiss, David. "Harmonic Analyzer Helps Solve Power Problems." *EC&M* (March, 1989).

Lawrie, Robert J. *Electrical Systems for Computer Installations.* New York, NY: McGraw-Hill Book Company, 1988.

McCoy, C. E. *Static Power Converters, Harmonics, The Power Systems and You.* 1986.

McEachern, Alexander. *Voltage, Current, Power Factor, and Spectrum Measurements on Non-sinusoidal AC Power*. Foster City, CA: Basic Measuring Instruments, 1987.

McGraw-Edison Power Systems, Cooper Industries, Inc. *Harmonic Considerations For Electrical Distribution Feeders*. Oak Ridge, TN: Oak Ridge National Laboratory, 1988.

McPartland Publishing. *Harmonics Handbook*. Englewood Cliffs, NJ: EJA International, 1991.

McPartland, Joseph F. *Handbook of Practical Electrical Design*. New York, NY: McGraw-Hill Book Company, 1983.

Messer, Inman and Pinkey. "Non-linear Loads: The UPS Solution." *AIPE Facilities* (January/February, 1992).

Meyer, Charles. *SCR-Controlled Loads, Waveform Distortion, and Standby Power Systems*. Onan Corp, 1987.

Newage Engineers Limited. *Impact of Non-Linear Loads On Stamford A.C. Generators*. [n.d.].

Newcombe, Charles and Ferguson, Gregory. *Measurement and Analysis for Zero Sequenced Harmonic Filter Application at Receptacle Load Centers*. 1993.

Price, Kenneth. *Energy Efficiency vs. Power Quality—Case Studies In Equipment Incompatibility*. ZM Communications, 1992.

Rice, David. "Adjustable Speed Drive and Power Rectifier Harmonics—Their Effect on Power Systems Components." *IEEE Transactions on Industry Applications* (January/February, 1986).

The 1989 *ARRL Handbook*. Newington, CT: The American Radio Relay League, 1988.

The Official Proceedings of Power Quality 89 (USA). Ventura, CA: Intertec Communications, 1989.

The Official Proceedings of Power Quality 90 (International). Ventura, CA: Intertec Communications, 1990.

The Official Proceedings of Power Quality 90 (Europe). Ventura, CA: Intertec Communications, 1990.

The Official Proceedings of Power Quality 91 (International). Ventura, CA: Intertec International, 1991.

The Official Proceedings of Power Quality 92 (International). Ventura, CA: Insystex, 1992.

The Official Proceedings of Power Quality 93 (International). Ventura, CA: Intertec International, 1993.

Troberg, Dick. "Hands-on Approach to Solving Harmonic Problems." *EC&M* (March ,1990).

Troberg, Dick. "Troubleshooting Harmonics In A Modern Office Building." *Electricity Today* (February, 1991).

Van Valkenburgh, Nooger & Neville, Inc. *Basic Electricity*. Indianapolis, IN: Prompt Publications, 1992.

Index